Elementary Computer
Applications
in science, engineering, and business

Elementary Computer Applications

in science, engineering, and business

Ian Barrodale, Ph.D.
Frank D. K. Roberts, Ph.D.
Byron L. Ehle, Ph.D.

Department of Mathematics
University of Victoria
Victoria, B.C., Canada

John Wiley & Sons Inc.

New York   London   Sydney   Toronto

Library of Congress Catalogue Card Number: 74–150609
ISBN 0–471–05422–4 (cloth)
ISBN 0–471–05423–2 (paper)

Printed in the United States of America.

10 9 8 7 6 5 4 3 2 1

Preface

This book provides an introduction to many of the computing techniques that are used in science, engineering, and business. A student who studies the contents carefully, and who also completes a reasonable selection of the many exercises provided, will gain considerable understanding of what computers can do in these areas. In addition, programming skills can be developed by working through the programming exercises and flowcharts of each chapter.

We teach from this material in a second semester course for first-year students at the University of Victoria. All of these students have previously learned to program a computer during their first semester, and many of them are enrolled simultaneously in an introductory calculus course. This book can also be used as a supplementary textbook in an introductory programming course in which some programming language (such as FORTRAN, BASIC, PL/1, or ALGOL) is taught. We have not included any computer programs, but instead we use flowcharts to illustrate most of the techniques discussed. Thus the entire book is independent of any particular programming language. Several of the chapters, and particularly the latter ones, require very little knowledge of mathematics. Indeed, the majority of the topics covered in this book could be presented in high schools.

The material is divided into three sections: numerical analysis, operations research, and data processing. We have arranged the text in this order so that the degree of complexity of the programming skills required increases through the book. The selection of topics within these three branches of computing science was influenced by our desire to present, at an introductory level, problems that are both practical and typical of these areas. One of our aims throughout has been to provide sufficient motivation via discussion, worked examples, and exercises, to encourage the reader towards further study in computing science. Although many straightforward exercises are provided in the text, several more demanding ones also occur at the end of each chapter.

It is a pleasure to acknowledge the encouragement and advice given to us by Professor T. E. Hull of the University of Toronto when we were designing the course for which this book was written. Subsequently, several of our colleagues and students in Victoria were kind enough to read parts of the manuscript and offer numerous suggestions for improvements. Further helpful comments and suggestions were made by Professor E. I. Organic (University of Houston), Professor W. S. Dorn (University of Denver), Professor G. N. Arnovick (Chico State College), and Mrs. Joan K. Hughes (IBM — Los Angeles). Finally, we wish to thank Miss Beverly Cooknell and Mrs. Lynn Stewart for their careful typing.

Ian Barrodale
Frank D. K. Roberts
Byron L. Ehle

Victoria, B.C.
January, 1971

Contents

Numerical
Analysis

Why study numerical analysis?

The chief role of modern numerical analysis is to facilitate the intelligent use of computers in solving mathematical problems numerically. These problems may arise in such diverse fields as economics, genetics, astronomy, city planning, nutrition, engineering, and ecology: in short, any discipline or activity that can be described, approximated, or analyzed mathematically.

The development of electronic computers has encouraged scientists to construct and manipulate more realistic mathematical models than were hitherto deemed feasible. For example, both the development and operation of atomic power plants and the manned flights to the moon were made possible by this dynamic progress in problem solving. Meanwhile, the increasing availability of computers has allowed universities, colleges, and high schools, to provide instruction in computer programming to students of many different ages and interests. Consequently, it is safe to predict that the future stockpile of practical problems suitable for computer solution will continue to enlarge rapidly, both in size and variety. Hopefully, the successful solution of these mathematical problems will constitute progress towards solving some of the important social and economic problems in medicine, agriculture, conservation of resources, education, and recreation.

We have chosen to present only three topics in this section, even though there are perhaps a dozen different subjects covered in most introductory textbooks on numerical analysis. However, most of these remaining areas do require a more advanced knowledge of mathematics than that assumed in our exposition. Even in a brief introduction to numerical analysis, it is not enough that a student merely learns to program an assortment of seemingly unrelated numerical methods. By concentrating our attention on just three topics, we are able to describe and compare two or three different methods for solving each problem, within the limited space available. In some cases, there may be precise reasons why a particular numerical method should be adopted. Usually this is not the case, and more than one method may be employed to solve a given problem. The ability to analyze the merits of existing and proposed numerical techniques is essential to intelligent computation.

A scientific programmer generally attempts to compute answers to a predetermined accuracy. For example, he may require an answer to a certain problem to be correct to five decimal places. Unfortunately, since computers represent numbers by just the first few digits of their decimal representations, this degree of accuracy may not be attainable, even though the numerical method involved may be extremely accurate when used with the real numbers of ordinary arithmetic. The error thus introduced by the computer is called rounding error, and when numbers are combined together thousands of times its presence can cause a serious loss of accuracy to occur in the final answer. The analysis of rounding error is one of the concerns of a numerical analyst. This problem plagues most scientific computations, and it is referred to several times in the chapters which follow.

3

1

Roots of Equations

1. Introduction

A fundamental problem in mathematics is that of finding the roots of a given equation. Consequently, in those computing centres which are involved in scientific computation, this problem often requires solution many times a day. In this chapter, we shall discuss how to solve on a computer equations of the form:

$$f(x) = 4x^5 - 3x^4 + 2x - 7 = 0 \qquad (1.1)$$

$$f(x) = x + \sin x - 3 = 0 \qquad (1.2)$$

$$f(x) = x^2 - 1.49237 = 0 . \qquad (1.3)$$

A root or solution of a general equation

$$f(x) = 0 \qquad (1.4)$$

is a number x which makes $f(x)$ equal to zero. We shall consider only real numbers x here, although it is usually not difficult to operate with complex numbers on most modern computers. A given equation (1.4) may have no roots, a single root, several roots, or even an infinite number of roots. It is called either a polynomial equation (see (1.1) and (1.3)) or else a transcendental equation (see (1.2)).

A general polynomial equation of the mth degree is of the form

$$f(x) = a_m x^m + a_{m-1} x^{m-1} + \cdots + a_1 x + a_0 = 0 \qquad (1.5)$$

5

where a_m, a_{m-1},...,a_0 are known constants. Exact methods that yield all the roots of (1.5) are known only for m = 1, 2, 3, and 4. For polynomials of higher degrees, and for almost all transcendental equations, we have to resort to indirect methods which yield approximate values for the desired roots. The methods discussed here apply equally to polynomial equations and transcendental equations, and they are all examples of iterative techniques.

Any iterative root-finding procedure is of the following general character. Starting with an equation (1.4) and an approximation x_1 to a root, we decide upon a rule or routine that will produce another approximation x_2. This rule may be constructed directly from the particular function f(x) under consideration, or it may be a general procedure which incorporates the given function f(x). In any event, the initial approximation can be regarded as the input for the procedure and the new approximation x_2 as its output. The approximation x_2 is then used as input, and the procedure produces another approximation x_3. This process is repeated over and over again, thus producing a sequence of approximations x_1, x_2, x_3, x_4 ... . The process is terminated as soon as two successive approximations are close enough to be considered equal, for all practical purposes, and the final approximation is taken as a root of the equation (1.4).

It is clear that an iterative scheme of this type is ideally suited for use on a high-speed computer. Indeed, although the methods presented here are several hundred years old, their true potential has not been realized until quite recently. However, in practice the behavior of these iterative methods is not quite so straightforward as the above presentation might suggest. The sequence of successive approximations may not be converging even after a large number of iterations; that is, no two successive numbers x_n and x_{n+1} get close enough together to be considered approximately equal. Also, even if a particular routine does produce a sequence $x_1, x_2, x_3,...$ which converges to some number x = α, it may be that α is not a root of f(x) = 0. When writing a computer program for an iterative root-finding method, we must allow for these possible shortcomings. If our method is not guaranteed to converge, it is necessary to include a safety feature in the program which terminates the computation after a prescribed number of iterations. If an approximation x = β to a root is produced, it is always a good idea to output the value of f(β) also. Finally, although the above simplified description of an iterative process involves a single input x_n and a single output x_{n+1}, several popular methods involve multiple input and output. Indeed, the first method we discuss requires as input two approximations, x_1 and x_2, which lie on either side of some root of f(x) = 0, while the output consists of two points which are closer together, but which similarly enclose a root.

We now proceed to describe three iterative methods for solving the equation (1.4). Throughout the discussion, we assume that the function f(x) is a continuous unbroken curve defined for all values of x.

2. The Method of Bisection

The method of bisection is a safe method, in the sense that it is guaranteed to produce a sequence of approximations which converges to some root of $f(x) = 0$.

The method requires that we start with two points x_1 and x_2, for which the function values $f(x_1)$ and $f(x_2)$ have opposite signs. Since $f(x)$ is a continuous curve there is at least one root between x_1 and x_2, as is the case in Figure 1a.

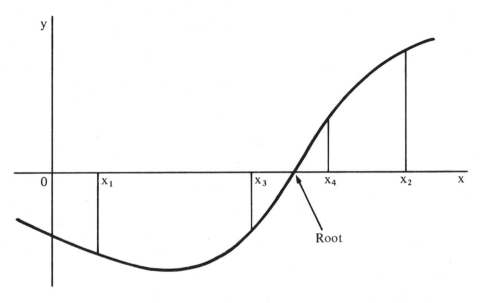

FIGURE 1a: Locating a root by the method of bisection.

This interval of uncertainty $[x_1, x_2]$ is then bisected, and the function $f(x)$ is evaluated at the midpoint $x_3 = (x_1 + x_2)/2$. If $f(x_3)$ has the same sign as $f(x_1)$, as in Figure 1a, then the new interval of uncertainty is $[x_3, x_2]$. A root is still trapped in this new interval, which is just one half the length of the first interval. The midpoint x_4 of $[x_3, x_2]$ is then located, and x_4 replaces either x_2 or x_3 according to the sign of $f(x_4)$. This process is continued until we reach an interval of uncertainty whose length is less than some preset small positive number δ. At this stage, the midpoint of the final interval approximates some root of $f(x) = 0$ to an accuracy of at least $\epsilon = \delta/2$.

When writing a computer program for the method of bisection, two slight modifications to the outline above are suggested. Firstly, rather than working with subscripted variables to represent the successive approximations, it is more convenient and economical to use just three variables x_1, x_2, and $\bar{x} = (x_1 + x_2)/2$. At each iteration either x_1 or x_2 is set equal to $\bar{x}$, according to the sign of $f(\bar{x})$. Secondly, the decision process which determines whether or not $f(\bar{x})$ has the same sign as $f(x_1)$, and which then assigns the value $\bar{x}$ to either x_1 or x_2 accordingly, can be handled conveniently by considering the sign of the product $f(x_1) f(\bar{x})$. The flowchart in Figure 1b describes the method of bisection as it might be implemented in practice. (Exercise 22 contains a suggested modification to Figure 1b; how important is this modification?)

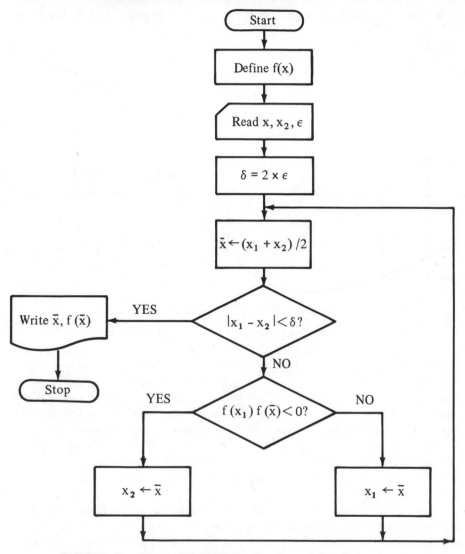

FIGURE 1b: The method of bisection for solving $f(x) = 0$.

Exercises

1. Using the method of bisection, with $\epsilon = 0.0005$, write a program to find a root of:

    a. $f(x) = x^2 - 7 = 0$ with $x_1 = 2$ and $x_2 = 3$.

    b. $f(x) = x^5 - 59 = 0$ with $x_1 = 2$ and $x_2 = 2.5$.

    c. $f(x) = 5 \sin x - 10x + 2 = 0$ with $x_1 = 0$ and $x_2 = 3$.

    d. $f(x) = x - 3^{-x} = 0$ with $x_1 = 0$ and $x_2 = 1$.

    e. $f(x) = x^2 + 10x \log x = 0$ with $x_1 = 0.1$ and $x_2 = 1$.

2. Calculate, correct to three decimal places, a root of
$$f(x) = e^x - (2x + 3)/(x^2 + 1) = 0$$

3. Solve $f(x) = x^{10} - 10^x = 0$ with $\epsilon = 10^{-5}$.

4. The method of bisection will not yield any real roots for $f(x) = x^2 - 2x + 2 = 0$. Why?

5. Find all three roots of $f(x) = 8x^3 + 2x^2 - 5x + 1 = 0$ correct to five decimal places.

3. The Method of Successive Approximations

Our second iterative procedure involves a preliminary rearrangement of the given equation (1.4), in order that the variable x appears explicitly. For example, the equation $f(x) = \sin 2x - x - 0.5 = 0$ may be rewritten as $x = \sin 2x - 0.5$. In general, suppose that equation (1.4) is rewritten as

$$x = F(x)$$

and, from an initial approximation x_1 to a root of (1.4), we define

$$x_2 = F(x_1)$$
$$x_3 = F(x_2)$$

.

.

.

and generally,

$$x_{n+1} = F(x)_n) \tag{1.6}$$

The rule (1.6) is usually referred to as the method of successive approximations. It is an example of a method which is tailored to suit the equation at hand. However, as might be expected, this procedure is not guaranteed to converge in general. On the other hand, if the successive approximations $x_1, x_2, x_3, \ldots$ finally terminate in a number α such that

$$\alpha = F(\alpha) \tag{1.7}$$

then α is a root of (1.4), since (1.7) can be rewritten as

$$f(\alpha) = 0$$

Example 1–1. Using the method of successive approximations, find, to an accuracy $\epsilon = 0.0005$, a root of

$$f(x) = x^2 - \sqrt{x} - 3 = 0 \qquad (1.8)$$

Equation (1.8) can be put into the form $x = F(x)$ in several ways. We take $x = F(x) = (3 + \sqrt{x})^{\frac{1}{2}}$, which suggests the iteration

$$x_{n+1} = (3 + \sqrt{x_n})^{\frac{1}{2}}. \qquad (1.9)$$

It is clear that there is a root of (1.8) between 1 and 3, and so we choose $x_1 = 2$. The following sequence of approximations is produced by applying (1.9) iteratively.

n	x_n
1	2.00000
2	2.10100
3	2.10938
4	2.11006
5	2.11012

Thus the root is 2.110, correct to three decimal places. The rapid convergence of the sequence $x_1, x_2, x_3, \ldots$ in this particular example cannot be guaranteed in general for this method.

A flowchart for the method of successive approximations is contained in Figure 1c. Notice that a preset limit, N, on the total number of iterations is used to halt the computation in case the sequence of approximations fails to converge.

Finally, we note that a condition is known that is sufficient to guarantee the convergence of the iterative rule (1.6) for a given function $F(x)$. By interpreting the method of successive approximations geometrically, as we have done in Figure 1d, it is not difficult to discover this condition ourselves. The condition is that the slope of $F(x)$, i.e. the derivative $F'(x)$, be less than 1 in absolute value, for all points in the interval which contains all the successive approximations $x_1, x_2, x_3, \ldots$. Since an equation (1.4) can usually be rearranged in several ways to give an equation of the form (1.6), including the addition of the quantity x to both sides of (1.4), it is sometimes necessary to try two or three different such rearrangements before convergence takes place.

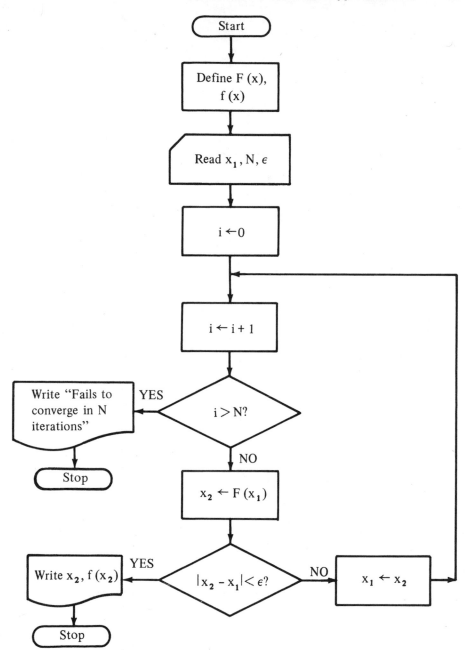

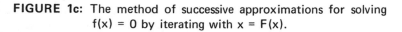

FIGURE 1c: The method of successive approximations for solving $f(x) = 0$ by iterating with $x = F(x)$.

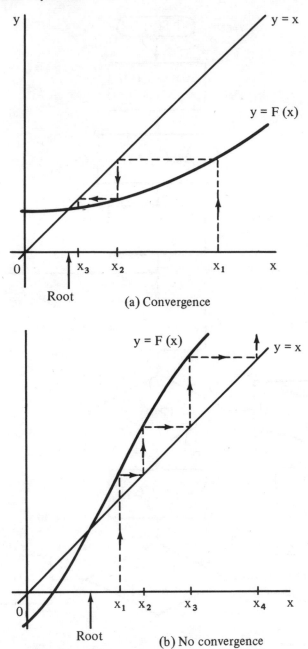

(a) Convergence

(b) No convergence

FIGURE 1d: The method of successive approximations converges provided that the slope of F(x) is not too steep.

Exercises

6. Using the method of successive approximations, with $N = 50$ and $\epsilon = 0.001$, write a program to find a root of:

    a. $f(x) = x - \sin x - 1 = 0$ with $x_1 = 1$
    b. $f(x) = x + e^x = 0$ with $x_1 = -1$
    c. $f(x) = x - \log x - 1.5 = 0$ with $x_1 = 2$
    d. $f(x) = x^2 - 0.41 = 0$ with $x_1 = 1$
    e. $f(x) = x - e^x/3$ with $x_1 = 2$

7. The equation $f(x) = x^2 - 5x + 4 = 0$ has roots at $x = 1$ and $x = 4$. The equation can be rearranged into the form $x = (x^2 + 4)/5$, thus defining an obvious iterative rule. Try to produce the root at $x = 4$, via this rule, choosing x_1 to be any number close to 4. If you are unsuccessful in reaching the root at $x = 4$, then try some other iterative rule based on the given equation.

8. Solve the equation $x = e^{-x}$ correct to four decimal places.

9. The equation $f(x) = x^2 - x = 0$ has roots at $x = 0$ and $x = 1$. The iteration $x_{n+1} = x_n^2$ is bound to converge to the smaller root if x_1 is chosen from a certain interval. What is this interval? Can the iteration $x_{n+1} = x_n^2$ ever converge to $x = 1$ provided that $x_1 \neq 1$?

10. Consider the equation $f(x) = x^2 - 10x + 24.5 = 0$. If the constant term of 24.5 contains an error whose absolute value is at most 1, will this have much effect on the solutions to the equation?

4. The Newton–Raphson Method

Both of the iterative methods discussed so far usually require a large number of iterations to converge to within reasonable accuracy. This is particularly true of the method of bisection, whereas the method of successive approximations will sometimes converge quickly. However, for this second method these instances of rapid convergence are probably outnumbered in practice by the occasions when the method does not converge at all. Provided that the function $f(x)$ is differentiable, the Newton–Raphson method usually converges for equations of the type (1.4), and its rate of convergence is almost always very rapid. The origin of this method is probably due to a picture similar to that of Figure 1e.

The method proceeds as follows. An initial approximation x_1 to a root of $(f(x) = 0)$ is first chosen. This approximation is then improved by defining,

$$x_2 = x_1 - d$$
$$= x_1 - f(x_1)/f'(x_1) \tag{1.10}$$

(Recall that the derivative $f'(x)$ measures the slope of the tangent line to $y = f(x)$, and that the slope of a line is its change in y per unit change in x). Continuing as in (1.10), we obtain the Newton-Raphson iterative root-finding procedure,

$$x_{n+1} = x_n - f(x_n)/f'(x_n)$$

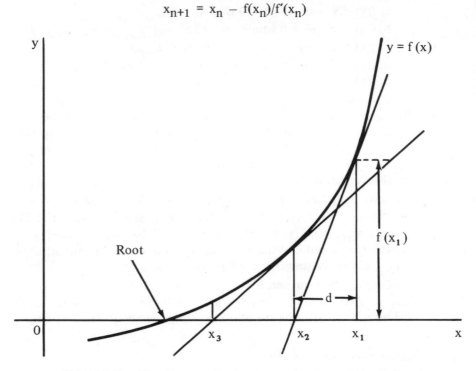

FIGURE 1e: The Newton–Raphson method for solving f(x) = 0.

Example 1–2. Calculate $\sqrt{3}$, correct to six decimal places, using the Newton-Raphson procedure to solve $f(x) = x^2 - 3 = 0$.

Since $f(x) = x^2 - 3$ and $f'(x) = 2x$, then (1.11) gives

$$x_{n+1} = x_n - (x_n^2 - 3)2x_n$$
$$= \frac{1}{2}(x_n + \frac{3}{x_n}) \qquad (1.12)$$

Taking $x_1 = 2$, the formula (1.12) gives the following sequence of approximations to $\sqrt{3}$.

n	x_n
1	2.00000000
2	1.75000000
3	1.73214286
4	1.73205081
5	1.73205081

Thus, to the accuracy required, $\sqrt{3} = 1.732051$. Notice in this example that the number of correct decimal places doubles in each successive iteration. This very rapid convergence is typical of the Newton-Raphson method. Indeed, this is the method whereby high-speed computers determine square roots, cube roots, etc., via an internal subprogram.

Unfortunately, the Newton-Raphson method is not guaranteed to converge for all problems of the type (1.4). However it does always converge, for example, when applied to the above problem of finding the q-th root of a given number. We shall not give the sufficient conditions for convergence here, but simply state that, in practice, the Newton-Raphson method usually converges, especially when the initial approximation x_1 is already close to a root of $f(x) = 0$. Furthermore, it is clear that if a sequence produced by (1.11) converges to α, then α is a root of (1.4).

Exercises

11. Draw a flowchart of the Newton-Raphson method, and then write a program to calculate (correct to four decimal places) a root of:

a. $f(x) = x^5 - 2 = 0$ with $x_1 = 1$.
b. $f(x) = x^7 - x^5 - x^3 - 1 = 0$ with $x_1 = 2$.
c. $f(x) = x^3 + 1.9x^2 - 1.3x - 2.2 = 0$ with $x_1 = 1$.
d. $f(x) = e^x - \tan x = 0$ with $x_1 = 1.5$.
e. $f(x) = x \sin x - \cos x = 0$ with $x_1 = 0.5$.

12. Find a root of $f(x) = \cosh x + \cos x - 2 = 0$ correct to six decimal places. (Recall that $\cosh x = (e^x + e^{-x})/2$).

13. Calculate all the roots of $f(x) = x^3 + 7.6x^2 + 11.8x - 6 = 0$ correct to three decimal places.

14. Using the Newton-Raphson method, compute the first ten approximations to the root of $f(x) = (x - 1)^2 = 0$, starting with $x_1 = 0.5$. Repeat this procedure with $g(x) = (x - 1)(x - 20) = 0$ and $x_1 = 0.5$. Although $x = 1$ is a root of both equations, notice that the successive approximations to the root of $g(x) = 0$ converge much faster than those for $f(x) = 0$. Can you explain this phenomenon?

15. Try the Newton-Raphson method for $f(x) = x^2 - 9x + 25 = 0$.

(Does your program contain an iteration counter, in case convergence has not occurred after a hundred or so iterations?)

5. Summary

The method of bisection is a very safe and sure technique for locating a root of a continuous function $f(x) = 0$. It is bound to converge to some root in the original interval $[x_1, x_2]$, but its rate of convergence is slow. Computationally, the approximate root $\bar{x}$ produced by this method satisfies $f(\bar{x} + d) = 0$, for some small number d. The successive approximation method is rather risky, unless we can be sure that the sufficient condition for convergence is satisfied. Even then, its rate of convergence may be slow for a given problem. The Newton–Raphson method is perhaps the most popular root-finding procedure known. It is more reliable than the method of successive approximations, and it almost always exhibits rapid convergence. However, it does require a knowledge of the derivative $f'(x)$, and this may be difficult to obtain in some practical problems. From the computational viewpoint, the accuracy attainable with the Newton–Raphson method depends upon the accuracy to which $f(x)/f'(x)$ can be computed.

Exercises

16. Repeat Exercise 6 using the Newton–Raphson method instead of the method of successive approximations. Compare the calculation times and the total number of iterations required by the two methods.

17. Sketch three different situations in which the sequence of iterates produced by the Newton–Raphson method fails to converge.

18. The reciprocal of a number K can be computed approximately without the operation of division. (In fact, some of the earliest computers lacked this operation, and a quotient m/n was calculated by first estimating the quantity 1/n and then multiplying it by m.) Show how this is accomplished by solving $f(x) = (1/x) - K = 0$ by the Newton–Raphson method, and hence calculate the reciprocal of $K = 2.71828182846$ correct to ten decimal places.

19. Find the points of intersection of the curves

$$y = e^x - 5, \qquad y = \log(x + 3)$$

correct to four decimals.

20. The equation $50x^4 - 185x^3 + 221x^2 - 185x + 171 = 0$ has two roots close to $x = 2$. Calculate these roots correct to five decimals. Try to calculate the roots of this equation with both coefficients of 185 changed to 184.8.

21. Determine, correct to four decimal places, a root of the equation

$f(x) = e^{cx} - 2.17893 = 0$, when

   a. $c = 1000$

   b. $c = 1/1000$.

Evaluate the function $f(x)$ for each computed root. Are these function values equal to zero to within four decimal places? Graph both functions in the neighbourhood of the roots.

22. In Figure 1b a flowchart for the method of bisection is supplied. Modify this flowchart so that the method terminates if $f(\bar{x})$ is actually equal to zero. What are the implications of a further modification which would terminate the calculations if $|f(\bar{x})| < \epsilon$? (Notice that the accuracy of any of these versions of the method of bisection is limited only by the accuracy with which $f(x)$ may be evaluated.)

23. Do any of the methods discussed in this chapter extend to the problem of finding a root of $f(x_1, x_2) = 0$?

24. Graph the function $f(x) = 4x^4 - 32x^3 + 89x^2 - 103x + 42$ for $0 \leqslant x \leqslant 5$, indicating to four correct decimals its relative maxima and minima, and the points at which it intersects the x-axis.

25. In designing a new gear system for a truck, an engineer needs to determine the smallest positive value of t at which the two curves $y = e^{-at}$ and $y = \sin bt$ intersect. Determine this point of intersection correct to three decimal places when $a = 2.178$ and $b = 0.982$. Check your answer using a second numerical method.

26. The average energy of vibration E of a molecule with frequency f depends on the temperature T according to the equation

$$E = \left\{ \frac{hf}{e^{hf/kT} - 1} \right\} + \frac{1}{2} hf$$

Here, $h = 6.626 \times 10^{-27}$ erg/sec. is Planck's constant and $k = 1.38 \times 10^{-16}$ erg/°K is Boltzmann's constant. Find the frequency f of a molecule for which $E = 3.97 \times 10^{-14}$ erg and $T = 310°K$.

27. In a chemical calculation of a weak base in a buffer solution the following equation occurs:

$$(OH-)^3 - 1.63 \times 10^{-6}(OH-)^2 - 2.47 \times 10^{-12}(OH-) - 2.80 \times$$

Calculate a solution to this equation to four significant figures.

28. The volume of 1 gram of a liquid at temperatures from $0°$ C. to $33°$ C. is given by the equation

$$V = 0.9999 - 6.43 \times 10^{-5}T + 8.505 \times 10^{-6}T^2 - 6.8 \times 10^{-8}T^3$$

where T is the temperature in degrees centigrade. Find the temperature at which the density (weight per unit volume) is a maximum.

29. An alternative iterative method for solving $f(x) = 0$ is the secant method. This can be obtained from the Newton–Raphson method by substituting the quotient $(f(x_n) - f(x_{n-1}))/(x_n - x_{n-1})$ for $f'(x_n)$ in expression (1.11). Notice that x_{n+1} is now calculated from two previous estimates x_n and x_{n-1}. The secant method is not guaranteed to converge to a root, and generally it requires more iterations than does the Newton–Raphson method. However, it is used in practice when derivatives are time-consuming to evaluate or very difficult to obtain.

    a. Repeat Exercise 1 using the secant method.

    b. Calculate the smallest positive root of $\tan x - \cos x = 0.5$ using the secant method.

30. Find out about numerical methods for calculating both the real and complex roots of the equation $f(x) = 0$.

31. Investigate the following:

    a. the Q–D method for calculating roots of polynomial equations;

    b. synthetic division for factoring out roots of polynomial equations;

    c. the effect on the roots of a polynomial equation of uncertainties in the coefficients.

Further Reading

Froberg, C. E., *Introduction to Numerical Analysis,* 2nd ed., Addison-Wesley, Reading, Mass., 1969.

McCracken, D. D. and W. S. Dorn, *Numerical Methods and FORTRAN Programming,* John Wiley, New York, 1964.

Ralston, A., *A First Course in Numerical Analysis,* McGraw-Hill, New York, 1965.

Scheid, F., *Theory and Problems of Numerical Analysis,* Schaum's Outline Series, McGraw-Hill, New York, 1968.

Traub, J. F., *Iterative Methods for the Solution of Equations,* Prentice-Hall, Englewood Cliffs, N. J., 1964.

Numerical
Integration

1. Introduction

Many students encounter the concept of a definite integral during their last years at high school or their first year at college. The introduction of the integral calculus some three hundred years ago is generally regarded as a milestone of mathematics. Today the need to evaluate integrals arises frequently in many areas of science, and, increasingly, the calculations involved are performed on a computer.

Geometrically, the meaning of a definite integral is quite easily explained. Consider the graph of the function $y = f(x)$ in Figure 2a. Let I denote the shaded area enclosed between the curve $y = f(x)$ and the x-axis, from $x = a$ to $x = b$. Then we write

$$I = \int_a^b f(x)\ dx \qquad (2.1)$$

and I is called the definite integral of $f(x)$ for the interval $[a, b]$. Referring now to Figure 2b, this area I can clearly be approximated by the sum of the areas of the rectangles, as shown. The rectangles are formed by subdividing the interval $[a, b]$ into n subintervals, each of width $h = (b - a)/n$, and constructing sides on the points x_i of height $f(x_1)$, $f(x_2)$,..., $f(x_n)$. This approximation to I becomes more accurate as we increase n, and the limit of this process defines the integral as:

19

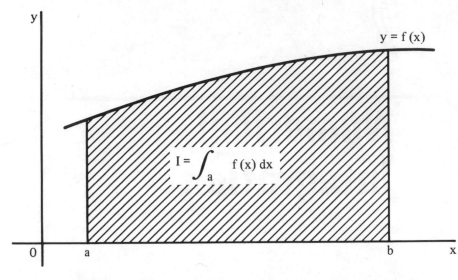

FIGURE 2a: Geometrical interpretation of a definite integral.

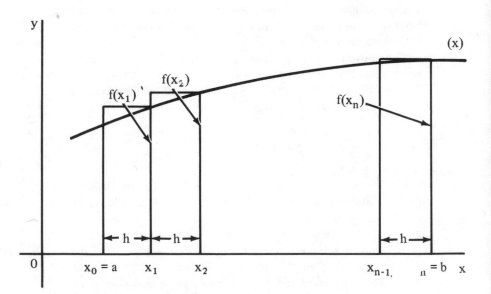

FIGURE 2b: The definite integral approximated by a sum of rectangles.

$$\int_a^b f(x)\ dx = I = \lim_{n \to \infty} (h\ f(x_1) + h\ f(x_2) + \cdots + h\ f(x_n))$$

$$= \lim_{n \to \infty} h \sum_{i=1}^n f(x_i) \qquad (2.2)$$

(The notation used in (2.2) is standard mathematical shorthand. The fact that n is increased in size without bound is denoted by $n \to \infty$, and the sum of several quantities is represented using a summation sign Σ).

For most of this chapter we assume that f(x) is a continuous nonnegative curve on the interval [a, b]. (It is not until Exercise 19 that negative-valued functions appear, while Exercise 22 involves the integral of a discontinuous function.) Now for many functions f(x), the integration methods taught in an introductory calculus course enable us to compute the quantity I in (2.1) exactly. Nevertheless, in practice we do encounter integrals that cannot be evaluated exactly without a great deal of effort, and sometimes not even then. Thus there is a need for approximate numerical methods of integration, and we shall study three such techniques here. The first two methods are capable of producing very accurate answers, and they are both based on the fundamental definition (2.2). The third technique is far less accurate in general, but it is applicable in some situations where more conventional numerical integration rules are difficult, or even impossible, to use.

2. The Trapezoidal Rule

Consider the integral (2.1), and let the interval [a, b] be divided into n sub-intervals of equal width h. Suppose that the function f(x) can be represented as in Figure 2c, where the area I is approximated by a sum of n trapezoids.

Then, if we denote by I_h the sum of the areas of the n trapezoids of width h, we can write:

$$I \simeq I_h = \frac{h}{2} (y_0 + y_1) + \frac{h}{2} (y_1 + y_2) + \cdots + \frac{h}{2} (y_{n-2} + y_{n-1}) + \frac{h}{2} (y_{n-1} + y_n)$$

$$= \frac{h}{2} (f(x_0) + 2f(x_1) + 2f(x_2) + \cdots + 2f(x_{n-2}) + 2f(x_{n-1}) + f(x_n)) \qquad (2.3)$$

where $h = (b - a)/n$.

The expression (2.3) for the approximate value of the integral I is called the trapezoidal rule.

Example 2–1. Evaluate $I = \int_0^1 x^2\ dx$ by using the trapezoidal rule with (a) h = 0.25 (b) h = 0.1.

$$I_{0.25} = \frac{0.25}{2} \left[0 + 2(0.25)^2 + 2(0.5)^2 + 2(0.75)^2 + 1 \right] = 0.34375$$

$$I_{0.1} = \frac{0.1}{2} \left[0 + 2(0.1)^2 + 2(0.2)^2 + \cdots + 2(0.9)^2 + 1 \right] = 0.33500$$

The exact value for I in this problem can be determined easily from the integral calculus. Thus, $I = 1/3 \simeq 0.33333$, and hence for this problem the trapezoidal rule with $h = 0.1$ gives a better approximation than with $h = 0.25$, which probably does not surprise the reader.

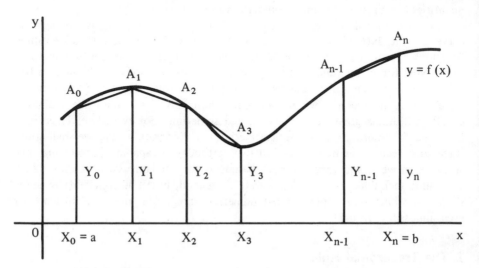

FIGURE 2c: Approximating an integral by a sum of n trapezoids.

Intuitively, it seems clear that the rule (2.3) should yield answers of higher and higher accuracy upon decreasing the width h of each trapezoid. Indeed, by using some relatively simple theorems from the calculus, it can be shown that the error introduced by using (2.3) to estimate I is roughly proportional to h^2. Therefore, by decreasing h the difference between I and I_h should decrease rapidly. However, there is a practical limit to how far we should decrease h, since this involves an increase in the amount of computation required. Indeed, if the number of subintervals is very large, say $n = 1000$, the rounding errors introduced by computing so many quantities may combine to cause a decrease in the overall accuracy of the method. (Recall that rounding errors are those errors which result from representing real numbers on a computer by just their first few digits.) Typically, the total error incurred in implementing the trapezoidal rule on a computer decreases as the number of subintervals increases, but only up to a critical number of subintervals. Thereafter, the error grows and the overall accuracy of the rule decreases. This phenomenon is illustrated in Figure 2d.

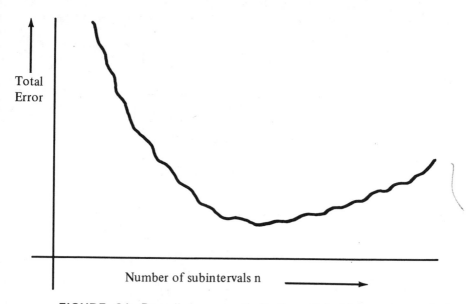

Total
Error

Number of subintervals n ⟶

FIGURE 2d: Rounding errors limit the attainable accuracy of the trapezoidal rule.

A computer program for the trapezoidal rule could be based on the flowchart in Figure 2e.

Exercises

1. Evaluate the following integrals numerically using the trapezoidal rule with n = 10, 50, and 200. Try to estimate the accuracy of your answers.

a. $\displaystyle\int_0^1 x^2 \, dx$

b. $\displaystyle\int_0^{\pi/2} \cos x \, dx$

c. $\displaystyle\int_1^5 (x^3 + 3x + 2) \, dx$

d. $\displaystyle\int_0^1 \sqrt{1 - \sin x} \, dx$

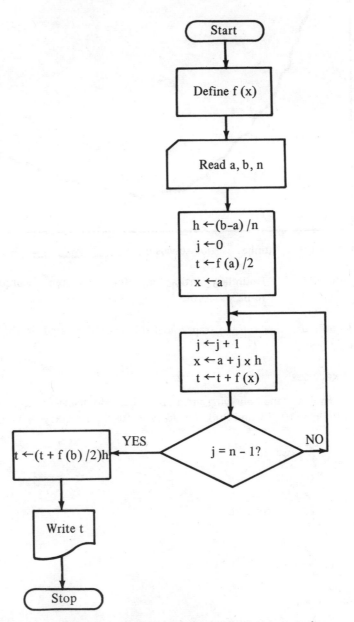

FIGURE 2e: The trapezoidal rule for numerical integration.

e. $\int_0^1 \dfrac{dx}{x^2 + 1}$

2. Apply the trapezoidal rule to compute the integral of the following function:

x	f(x)
0	0.00000
$\pi/12$	0.25882
$2\pi/12$	0.50000
$3\pi/12$	0.70711
$4\pi/12$	0.86603
$5\pi/12$	0.96593
$\pi/2$	1.00000

Do you recognize this function?

3. Consider the integral

$$\int_1^2 \sqrt{x}\ dx\ .$$

Estimate the value of this integral to two decimal places by using the trapezoidal rule with n = 10, 20, 40, 80,... . That is, starting with n = 10, double the value of n several times until the corresponding estimates produced by the trapezoidal rule agree to two decimal places.

4. The integral

$$\int_0^1 (7 - 7x^6)\ dx = 6\ .$$

Use the trapezoidal rule with n = 2, 4, 8, 16, 32, 64,..., 4096 $(=2^{12})$ to estimate this integral, and calculate the error at each stage using the fact that the exact answer is 6. Which is the critical value for n in this problem? Repeat these calculations in multi-precision arithmetic.

5. Evaluate the integral

$$\int_1^2 (\sqrt{\sin x + 2xe^x + 3} + \log 4x)\ dx$$

by the trapezoidal rule to four decimal places.

3. Simpson's Rule

If the sequence of straight line segments $A_0 A_1$, $A_1 A_2$, $A_2 A_3$,... in Figure 2c gives a good approximation to the shape of the curve y = f(x), then the trapezoidal rule can provide answers of high accuracy without requiring n to be too large. In general, though, we would expect better accuracy to result from a rule which employs a sequence of curves passing through the points A_0, A_1, A_2, A_3,... . Simpson's rule is based on this assumption.

Here, we take the subintervals two at a time, and pass a quadratic curve through A_0, A_1, A_2, another quadratic through A_2, A_3, A_4, and so on. The sum of the areas under each of these quadratics is then taken as I_h, which is an approximation to I. Simpson's rule can be written as:

$$I \simeq I_h = \frac{h}{3}(y_0 + 4y_1 + y_2) + \frac{h}{3}(y_2 + 4y_3 + y_4) + \cdots + \frac{h}{3}(y_{n-2} + 4y_{n-1} + y_n)$$

$$= \frac{h}{3}(f(x_0) + 4f(x_1) + 2f(x_2) + 4f(x_3) + 2f(x_4) + \cdots + 2f(x_{n-2})$$

$$+ 4f(x_{n-1}) + f(x_n)) \tag{2.4}$$

where n is an even number, and h = (b − a)/n.

Now, although the motivation for Simpson's rule is, essentially, that a sequence of curves should approximate another curve better than a sequence of straight line segments, we cannot guarantee that Simpson's rule will always produce better accuracy than the trapezoidal rule. (Why?) The error introduced in estimating I by (2.4) can be shown to be roughly proportional to h^4, so clearly this error does decrease far more rapidly than for the trapezoidal rule. Typically, for the same value of n, Simpson's rule usually provides answers containing about twice as many correct decimal places as those given by the trapezoidal rule.

In implementing a numerical integration rule on a computer, a common practice is to choose the number of subintervals n arbitrarily, and then double n and repeat the calculations. This process is continued until comparable values for the integral are obtained, or until the necessity for a more powerful integration method becomes obvious.

Exercises

6. Evaluate the following integrals numerically using Simpson's rule with n = 10, 50, and 200. Estimate the accuracy of your answers by any means available.

a. $\int_0^1 x^3 \, dx$

b. $\int_0^\pi \sqrt{\sin x} \, dx$

c. $\int_1^3 x^2 e^x \, dx$

d. $\int_1^4 e^{\log\sqrt{x}} \, dx$

e. $\int_0^\pi \dfrac{dx}{2 + \cos x}$

7. Integrate the following function by Simpson's rule:

x	f(x)
0.00	1.0000
0.05	1.0513
0.10	1.1052
0.15	1.1618
0.20	1.2214
0.25	1.2840
0.30	1.3499
0.35	1.4191
0.40	1.4918

Is this function familiar to you?

8. Estimate

$$\int_0^{4\pi} \log(2 + x)|\sin 8x| \, dx$$

using Simpson's rule with n = 16, 32, 64, 128, 256, and 1024. Any comments?

9. Use Simpson's rule to calculate

$$\int_0^1 e^{-e^{-x}} \, dx$$

correct to four decimal places.

10. Verify by Simpson's rule that to four decimal places,

$$\int_0^{\pi/2} \sqrt{1 - \frac{1}{2}\sin^2 x} \, dx = 1.3506.$$

4. Numerical Integration by Monte Carlo Methods

It is not possible to produce sequences of truly random numbers on a computer. However, in a deterministic manner, we can produce sequences of numbers which are reasonably uniformly distributed between their lowest and highest members, and which occur in a "random" order.

The following random number generator produces two-digit numbers between 0 and 99 in a "random sequence." Take $x_0 = 3$, and define x_1 as the last two digits of $13x_0$. Put $x_0 = x_1$, and again x_1 is taken to be the last two digits of $13x_0$. Continue in this iterative manner, until the number 3 occurs again. The sequence thus produced is:

$$03, 39, 07, 91, 83, 79, 27, 51, 63, 19,$$
$$47, 11, 43, 59, 67, 71, 23, 99, 87, 31.$$

After 31 the sequence begins again at 03.

The numbers in this sequence are typical of what are known as random numbers. They are reasonably uniformly spaced between 0 and 99, there are approximately the same number of pairwise increases as decreases, double increases as double decreases, and so on. There are, in fact, several statistical tests which can be employed to determine the effectiveness of a proposed random number generator. Most computing centres have at least one program available which generates random numbers; usually such a program is available as a subprogram, which the user can utilize without having to concern himself with the mathematical details involved.

How can a sequence of random numbers serve to provide approximate values for definite integrals? The answer to this question can be found by interpreting the definite integral as an area under a curve. Suppose that we wish to compute the shaded area in Figure 2f, which corresponds to the integral of a positive function $f(x)$ which never exceeds a given number M on the interval $[a, b]$.

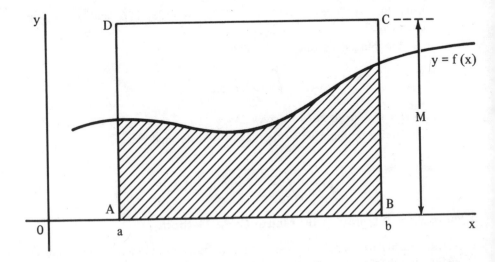

FIGURE 2f: Estimating a definite integral by a Monte Carlo method.

The rectangle ABCD is constructed on the interval [a, b] with height M; its area is thus $M(b - a)$. Suppose now that we throw darts at the rectangle ABCD in a random manner, and that we count both the total number that hit the rectangle and those that hit the shaded area. Then as the number of throws increases, the ratio of darts in the shaded area to the total number in the rectangle provides us with a reasonable estimate of the area of the shaded region as a proportion of the quantity $M(b - a)$. To implement this method on a computer we need, corresponding to each throw of a dart, two random numbers x and y, where x is from the interval [a, b] and y is in [0, M]. To determine whether the point (x, y) belongs to the shaded area we compute the quantity y $- f(x)$. If this number is positive then the point (x, y) does not belong to the shaded area. If $y - f(x)$ is zero or negative, this corresponds to a dart which hits the shaded area. By generating a few thousand such random pairs (x, y), and by forming the ratio of pairs for which $y \leqslant f(x)$ to the total number of pairs, this proportion of the number $M(b - a)$ usually provides a value for the definite integral which is accurate to within a few percent.

The above technique is quite easy to program, and a flowchart is provided in Figure 2g which assumes the availability of a random number generator.

This procedure is a typical Monte Carlo method, in that we are using a sampling technique to obtain a probabilistic approximation to the solution of a mathematical problem. The answers provided by the method are not very accurate, but for some complicated integrals that occur in practice this type of method is the only feasible technique available.

Finally, a variation on the method outlined above is worthy of mention since it yields a more efficient and simpler program. This modification relies upon the definition (2.2) for its motivation. We first observe that the following approximation,

$$\int_a^b f(x)\, dx = \lim_{n \to \infty} h \sum_{i=1}^n f(x_i)$$

$$\simeq \frac{(b-a)}{N} \sum_{i=1}^N f(x_i), \qquad (2.5)$$

can be quite accurate for a very large number N.

The method requires that we generate N random numbers x_i from the interval [a, b], and compute the quantity (2.5). We can simulate the process of taking the limit by choosing N to be suitably large, and thereby obtain an answer of reasonable accuracy.

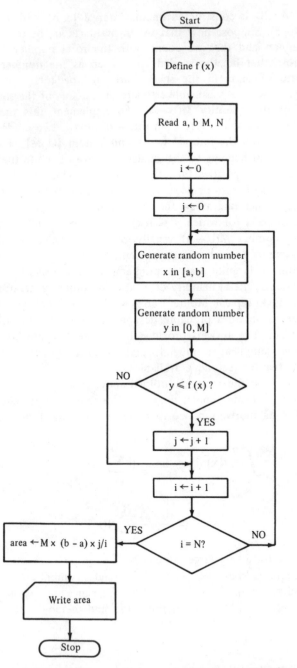

FIGURE 2g: A Monte Carlo method for numerical integration.

Exercises

11. Estimate the following integrals numerically by using a Monte Carlo method with N = 50, 200, and 1000.

a. $\int_0^1 x^2 \, dx$

b. $\int_{-3}^7 (5 + 3x)^4 \, dx$

c. $\int_0^{\pi/2} \sqrt{\cos x} \, dx$

d. $\int_0^1 x^{2/3} (x^{5/3} + 1)^{2/3} \, dx$

e. $\int_0^e \frac{e^{2x} \, dx}{\sqrt[3]{1 + e^x}}$

12. Geometrically, it is obvious that $\int_0^1 x \, dx = 0.5$. Using the more efficient Monte Carlo method referred to above, estimate this integral with N = 10, 40, 160, 640, and 2560.

13. Two points are chosen at random in a square with sides of length 1. Estimate the probability that they are more than 1/2 unit apart. (Recall that the distance between the points (x_1, y_1) and (x_2, y_2) is

$$\sqrt{(x_1 - x_2)^2 + (y_1 - y_2)^2} \quad).$$

14. Suppose we write

$$\int_0^1 \int_0^1 f(x, y) \, dx \, dy \simeq \frac{1}{N} \sum_{i=1}^N f(x_i, y_i),$$

where N is a large number of random pairs (x_i, y_i). Estimate the double integral $\int_0^1 \int_0^1 (x^2 + y^2) \, dx \, dy$ for N = 50, 200, and 800. (This double integral measures the volume of the solid region defined by z = f(x, y), the xy-plane, and the vertical sides defined by $0 \leqslant x \leqslant 1$ and $0 \leqslant y \leqslant 1$.)

15. Estimate the multiple integral

$$\int_0^1 \int_0^1 \int_0^1 \int_0^1 \frac{dW \, dX \, dY \, dZ}{1 + W + X + Y + Z}$$

using a Monte Carlo technique.

5. Summary

Simpson's rule is one of the most popular methods for numerical integration in use today. It usually provides satisfactory answers in fewer evaluations of the function f(x) than would be required by the trapezoidal rule. Both methods can give poor results if the computation is carried too far by increasing the number n unreasonably. Monte Carlo methods offer an intuitively simple approach at the expense of low accuracy. However they sometimes provide answers when other methods prove to be too unwieldy, particularly where multiple integrals are involved.

Exercises

16. Repeat Exercise 1 using Simpson's rule, and Exercise 6 using the trapezoidal rule. Compare the relative accuracy of the two numerical integration rules for all these integrals for which you know the exact answer.

17. If rounding errors are ignored, the value given by the trapezoidal rule for the integral $\int_a^b f(x)\, dx$ can be shown to deviate from the true value by no more than $h^2(b-a)M/12$, where

$$M = \max_{a \leqslant x \leqslant b} |f''(x)|.$$

(Here, the subintervals are of width $h = (b - a)/n$, and $f''(x)$ denotes the continuous second derivative with respect to x of the given function f(x).) The corresponding error bound for Simpson's rule is $h^4(b-a)K/180$ where

$$K = \max_{a \leqslant x \leqslant b} |f''''(x)|.$$

How well do these error bounds estimate the actual errors investigated in Exercise 16? It is possible to supply a bound corresponding to the rounding errors made in using either the trapezoidal rule or Simpson's rule on a computer. Both of these bounds are proportional to $1/h$. What does this suggest will happen as the number n of subintervals increases?

18. Sketch a function $y = f(x)$ on $[a, b]$ for which the trapezoidal rule provides a more accurate estimate for the integral

$$\int_a^b f(x)\, dx$$

than does Simpson's rule. Let n be the same fixed number of subintervals in both rules.

19. The functions f(x) considered thus far have not assumed negative values in the range of interest. From the definition of the definite integral, it is clear that a function f(x) which is negative on the interval [a, b] has a negative-valued integral. Thus, the integral $\int_{-2}^{0}$ x dx is equal to (−1). Furthermore, the integral $\int_{-1}^{+1}$ x dx is zero, even though the area bounded by the function f(x) = x, and the x-axis from x = −1 to x = 1, is equal to 1. Use Simpson's rule to estimate, correct to three decimal places, the areas bounded by:

    a. f(x) = x(x − 1)(x − 2)(x − 3), and the x-axis from x = −1 to x = 5.
    b. f(x) = sin x, and the x-axis from x = −2 to x = 1.
    c. f(x) = (x − 1)/(x + 1), and the x-axis from x = 0 to x = 2.

20. Estimate numerically the area between the lines x = −1, x = 1, and the curve $y^2(x^2 + 1) = x^2$. (Hint: Sketch the curve before you calculate the integral.)

21. Estimate numerically the area of the region bounded by the two curves y = x^4 and y = 3x + 10. (Hint: The points of intersection of these curves can be found numerically by solving f(x) = x^4 − 3x − 10 = 0.)

22. Estimate the integral

$$\int_0^3 \frac{dx}{\sqrt{|x-1|}}$$

using the trapezoidal rule. (A judicious choice for n can save you from some embarrassment here!)

23. Using a Monte Carlo technique, estimate

    a. $\int_{-1}^{+1} \int_{-1}^{+1} e^{-(x^2+y^2)} \, dx \, dy$

    b. $\iint_D \frac{dx \, dy}{(x^2 + y^2)}$,

where D is a square with corners (1,1), (3,1), (3,3), and (1,3).

24. Monte Carlo techniques become more efficient (or less inefficient!), relative to other numerical integration methods, as the multiplicity of an integral increases. Indeed, for most m-tuple integrals with m > 6 that occur in practice, there are no satisfactory alternative methods. The low accuracy typical of a Monte Carlo estimate is explained by the fact that the error is approximately proportional to $1/\sqrt{N}$, where N is the number of function evaluations involved. Thus, to achieve a ten-fold increase in accuracy requires that N be increased to about a hundred times its last value.

Estimate the 8-tuple integral

$$\int_0^1 \int_0^1 \cdots \int_0^1 \frac{dx_1 \, dx_2 \, \cdots \, dx_8}{1 + x_1 + x_2 + \cdots + x_8}$$

using a Monte Carlo technique. Use several increasing values for N until two successive estimates agree to within 0.01. Will your final answer necessarily be correct to within 0.01?

25. A portion of the geometric structure of a certain fish virus resembles the shape of a corkscrew. The length L of this space curve is given by

$$L = 2 \int_0^{a/c} \sqrt{\frac{b^2}{a^2} (a^{2n} - (cx)^{2n})^{1/n} \left[1 + \frac{x^{4n-2}}{(a^{2n} - (cx)^{2n})^2}\right] + c^2} \; dx$$

Using two different numerical methods, estimate L correct to two decimal places when a = 1.5, b = 1.2, c = 2.0, and n = 1.85.

26. If a variable force f(x) changes continuously when it is used to move a body along a line from x = a to x = b, the amount of work done is $W = \int_a^b f(x) \, dx$.

A gardener pulling an old wheelbarrow 100 feet along a straight path fails to notice that the contents are slowly leaking out. The wheelbarrow weighs 45 pounds, and the contents originally weighed 120 pounds. Assume that the force needed to pull the wheelbarrow is equal to one quarter of the total weight, and that the amount which has leaked out is proportional to the square-root of the distance travelled. If he loses one-sixth of the contents along the way, estimate numerically the amount of work done in moving the wheelbarrow.

27. A function which is important in statistical mechanics and in the kinetic theory of gases is denoted by erf(x), and is defined as erf(x) = $(2/\sqrt{\pi}) \int_0^x e^{-t^2} \, dt$. Notice that erf(x), which is called the error function, is defined by a definite integral. This integral cannot be evaluated analytically by the methods taught in an introductory calculus course. Construct a table of values for erf(x) with x = 0.1, 0.2,...,1.0, expressing these values to five decimal places. Check the accuracy of your computed table by consulting a table for erf(x) in a handbook of mathematical functions.

28. A physicist obtains the following table of data from an experiment:

x	0.2	0.3	0.4	0.5	0.6	0.7	0.8	0.9	1.0
y	1.21	1.47	1.82	2.01	2.17	2.25	2.51	2.98	3.14

Although y is an unknown function of x, he needs to find the area under the curve represented approximately by this table. Calculate this area using:

a. the trapezoidal rule.

b. Simpson's rule.

Without knowing more about this data, can you say which of these two answers is the more appropriate?

29. The trapezoidal rule and Simpson's rule are the first two in a sequence of numerical integration methods. Find out what the next rule in this sequence is.

30. The first error bound given in Exercise 17 implies that the trapezoidal rule can integrate exactly a linear function $f(x) = a + bx$, provided that rounding errors are ignored. For what functions is Simpson's rule exact?

31. A family of numerical integration rules due to Gauss provides alternative methods for integrating many functions very accurately. Find out about these rules. Why are they usually not applicable when tabulated data is involved, as in Exercise 28?

Further Reading

Abramowitz, M. and I. A. Stegun (eds.), *Handbook of Mathematical Functions,* National Bureau of Standards, App. Math. Series No. 55, Government Printing Office, Washington, 1964.

Davis, P. J. and P. Rabinowitz, *Numerical Integration,* Blaisdell, Waltham, Mass., 1967.

Froberg, C. E., *Introduction to Numerical Analysis,* 2nd ed., Addison-Wesley, Reading, Mass., 1969.

Householder, A. S., *Principles of Numerical Analysis,* McGraw-Hill, New York, 1953.

McCracken, D. D. and W. S. Dorn, *Numerical Methods and FORTRAN Programming,* John Wiley, New York, 1964.

Scheid, F., *Theory and Problems of Numerical Analysis,* Schaum's Outline Series, McGraw-Hill, New York, 1968.

Systems of Equations

1. Introduction

Systems of equations frequently arise during the formulation or the attempted solution of various problems from the physical and biological sciences, engineering, applied mathematics, and even the social sciences. A solution to a set or system of equations is a simultaneous solution, in that it must satisfy each equation individually. Thus $x = 3$ and $y = -2$ provide a solution to the system (3.1),

$$2x + y = 4$$
$$x + y = 1$$
(3.1)

whereas $x = 2$ and $y = 0$ satisfy only the first equation, and do not therefore constitute a solution to (3.1). A given set of equations may have no solution, exactly one solution, several solutions, or perhaps an infinite number of solutions. Linear systems of equations, such as (3.1) and (3.2),

$$10x_1 + x_2 - x_3 = 20$$
$$x_1 + 10x_2 + x_3 = 13$$
$$x_1 + 2x_2 + 5x_3 = 9$$
(3.2)

can usually be solved successfully either by hand calculation or on a computer. A nonlinear problem, say that of calculating a simultaneous solution to the system (3.3),

37

$$x_1 x_2 + 3^{x_2} = 11$$
$$x_1 \sin(\pi x_2/4) = 1 \tag{3.3}$$

is normally very difficult to handle. Indeed, the development of satisfactory techniques for solving systems of nonlinear equations on a computer is the object of a good deal of current research activity in numerical analysis.

In this chapter we shall only concern ourselves with numerical methods for solving linear systems of equations. Furthermore, we shall assume that these linear systems are inhomogeneous, which simply means that the right-hand members of the equations are not all zero.

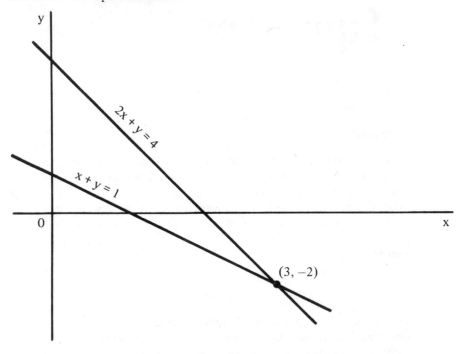

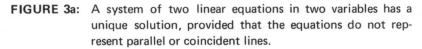

FIGURE 3a: A system of two linear equations in two variables has a unique solution, provided that the equations do not represent parallel or coincident lines.

A small linear system such as (3.1) can be represented geometrically, as in Figure 3a, since each equation defines a line and the solution to (3.1) corresponds to the point of intersection of both lines. Unless the two lines are parallel (no solution) or coincident (infinitely many solutions), there is exactly one solution to a system of two linear equations in two unknown variables x and y. Similarly, the system (3.2) can be interpreted as representing the equations of three planes, and again we may anticipate a unique solution. For general systems of linear equations, where a geometric interpretation may not be meaningful, we can sometimes rely upon an arithmetic criterion for information concerning the existence and uniqueness of solutions. This involves the concept of determinants.

The determinant of the system (3.1), which is written as

$$\begin{vmatrix} 2 & 1 \\ 1 & 1 \end{vmatrix}$$

is a number which is obtained by subtracting the diagonal products of the coefficients of x and y according to the rule:

$$\begin{vmatrix} a & b \\ c & d \end{vmatrix} = ad - bc. \tag{3.4}$$

Thus, for (3.1) we have that,

$$\begin{vmatrix} 2 & 1 \\ 1 & 1 \end{vmatrix} = 2 \times 1 - 1 \times 1 = 1.$$

The determinant of a system of three linear equations can then be calculated from its coefficients, as

$$\begin{vmatrix} a & b & c \\ d & e & f \\ g & h & i \end{vmatrix} = a \begin{vmatrix} e & f \\ h & i \end{vmatrix} - b \begin{vmatrix} d & f \\ g & i \end{vmatrix} + c \begin{vmatrix} d & e \\ g & h \end{vmatrix} \tag{3.5}$$

The determinant of the system (3.2) is 484; this can be verified using (3.5).

For a larger system of equations the determinant is similarly defined in terms of determinants of successively lower orders. The importance of the determinant lies in the fact that a given inhomogeneous system of linear equations has a unique solution if and only if its determinant is not zero.

In most introductory texts in linear algebra, following a more thorough discussion of determinants than that given here, a technique for expressing the solution to a set of linear equations via determinants is supplied. This analytic solution, which is referred to as Cramer's rule, is almost never computed in practice for systems of more than five or six equations. This is primarily because the evaluation of a higher order determinant requires an excessive amount of computation, and more economical methods of solution are available. For this same reason, the usefulness of the determinant in deciding whether or not a given set of equations has a unique solution is limited to relatively small systems. Fortunately, for many large problems that occur in practice the existence of a unique solution is guaranteed by other considerations.

In the next two sections we shall discuss two popular methods for solving a general system (3.6) of n linear equations:

$$a_{1,1}x_1 + a_{1,2}x_2 + \cdots + a_{1,n}x_n = b_1$$

$$a_{2,1}x_1 + a_{2,2}x_2 + \cdots + a_{2,n}x_n = b_2$$

$$\qquad \cdot \qquad \cdot \qquad\qquad \cdot \qquad \cdot$$
$$\qquad \cdot \qquad \cdot \qquad\qquad \cdot \qquad \cdot \qquad\qquad (3.6)$$
$$\qquad \cdot \qquad \cdot \qquad\qquad \cdot \qquad \cdot$$

$$a_{n,1}x_1 + a_{n,2}x_2 + \cdots + a_{n,n}x_n = b_n$$

In (3.6) the n unknowns x_1 $x_2,...,x_n$ have to satisfy the n linear equations formed from the known constants $a_{1,1}$, $a_{2,1},...,a_{n,n}$, b_1, $b_2,...,b_n$, where at least one b_i is not zero. An application of one of these techniques to the problem of least-squares estimation of data is then developed in the final section of this chapter.

Exercises

1. Evaluate the following determinants:

a. $\begin{vmatrix} 7 & 8 \\ 2 & 4 \end{vmatrix}$

b. $\begin{vmatrix} 40 & 4 \\ 17 & 2 \end{vmatrix}$

c. $\begin{vmatrix} 1 & 2 & 4 \\ 8 & -1 & 0 \\ 3 & 6 & 12 \end{vmatrix}$

2. Solve the following system of equations graphically

$$x + 2y = 2$$
$$7x - 4y = -13.$$

3. Can a system of linear equations have more than one solution? Exactly two solutions?

4. The set of equations

$$10.0x_1 + 7.0x_2 = 2.0$$
$$7.0x_1 + 5.0x_2 = 8.0$$

arises during a certain experiment in physics, and the coefficients in these equations are accurate to within ± 0.1. Do these small errors matter very much? Justify your answer graphically.

5. How many multiplications are required to evaluate the determinant of the general system (3.6) when n = 2, 3, 4, 10, 50? Assuming the availability of a very fast modern computer which can perform one million multiplications per second, how many years are required to evaluate the determinant when n = 50?

2. The Gauss-Seidel Iterative Method

This first technique is an extension to a system of equations of the method of successive approximations described in Chapter 1. It is best introduced by solving an actual problem.

Example 3–1. Using the Gauss-Seidel method, compute the solution to the system of equations (3.2),

$$10x_1 + x_2 - x_3 = 20$$
$$x_1 + 10x_2 + x_3 = 13$$
$$x_1 + 2x_2 + 5x_3 = 9$$

Iterate until the process converges to within an accuracy of 0.0001.

We proceed by expressing x_1 explicitly via the first equation, then x_2 via the second equation, and an expression for x_3 is obtained from the third equation. Thus, the given system is rearranged as

$$x_1 = \frac{1}{10} (20 - x_2 + x_3)$$
$$x_2 = \frac{1}{10} (13 - x_1 - x_3) \tag{3.7}$$
$$x_3 = \frac{1}{5} (9 - x_1 - 2x_2) .$$

The method consists of using the equations (3.7) as iteration rules for computing a solution to (3.2). Accordingly, we assign x_2 and x_3 arbitrary initial values, and compute x_1 from the first equation in (3.7). This value for x_1 is then inserted into the second equation, along with the initial value for x_3, and hence a new value for x_2 is produced. Similarly, a new value for x_3 is calculated from the third equation by employing the current values of x_1 and x_2. Each iteration of the Gauss-Seidel method involves one complete pass through all of the re-arranged equations, utilizing the most recent values for the unknown variables at each stage. The calculations are continued until convergence is obtained, or until a predetermined number of iterations has been completed. For this method, convergence occurs when for two successive iterations the absolute value of the difference between the successive values of each variable is less than a specified tolerance.

By setting both x_2 and x_3 initially to zero, the following sequence of approximations to the solution of the system (3.2) is obtained by applying the equations (3.7) iteratively.

Iteration number n	x_1	x_2	x_3
0		0	0
1	2.00000	1.10000	0.96000
2	1.98600	1.00540	1.00064
3	1.99952	0.99998	1.00010
4	2.00001	0.99999	1.00000
5	2.00000	1.00000	1.00000

After five iterations the value of each variable agrees with its previous value to well within the specified accuracy of 0.0001. It is clear that the exact solution is $x_1 = 2$, $x_2 = 1$, and $x_3 = 1$.

The Gauss-Seidel method for solving the general system of linear equations (3.6) is an interesting technique to program for a computer. Rather than supplying a detailed flowchart for such a project, we shall instead provide the complete sequence of operations which serve to define the method. The reader should be able to write a general program for Gauss-Seidel iteration after studying this sequential summary.

The rules for the method are expressed in terms of the quantities appearing in the general system (3.6). In addition, N is the maximum number of iterations allowed, and ϵ is the small positive number which determines when convergence has occurred.

(a) Read n, N, ϵ

(b) Read $a_{i,j}$ for i=1, 2,...,n; j=1, 2,...,n.

(c) Read b_i for i=1, 2,...,n

(d) Read (initial estimates) x_i for i=1, 2,...,n

(e) iter $\leftarrow 0$

(f) iter $\leftarrow$ iter + 1

(g) iter $> N$? If YES then write "no convergence" and go to step (j)

(h) $y_i \leftarrow (b_i - \displaystyle\sum_{\substack{j=1 \\ j\neq i}}^{n} a_{i,j}x_j)/a_{i,i}$

$d_i \leftarrow |x_i - y_i|$ $\left.\right\}$ $i=1, 2,..., n.$

$x_i \leftarrow y_i$

(i) $\max_i d_i > \epsilon$? If YES then return to step (f)

(j)   Write x_i for $i=1, 2,..., n.$

An experienced programmer will recognize that steps (h) and (i) together can be implemented in several different ways, depending upon possible restrictions imposed by storage allocation or calculation time on a particular computer. Notice also that we do supply an initial estimate for x_1. (Why?)

Finally, we note that a sufficient condition for convergence of this iterative technique is known. A determinant is said to be diagonally dominant if the absolute value of each diagonal entry (upper-left to lower-right) is greater than or equal to the sum of the absolute values of the entries in its row. In addition, for at least one row the diagonal entry must be strictly greater than its corresponding row sum in absolute value. Thus, the determinant

$$\begin{vmatrix} a & b & c \\ d & e & f \\ g & h & i \end{vmatrix}$$

is diagonally dominant provide that

$$|a| \geqslant |b| + |c|$$
$$|e| \geqslant |d| + |f|$$
$$|i| \geqslant |g| + |h|$$

with strict inequality holding in at least one of these constraints. For any irreducible system of linear equations (3.6) with a diagonally dominant determinant, it can be proved that the Gauss-Seidel iterative method is guaranteed to converge to the solution from arbitrary initial estimates for x_1, x_2,...,x_n. (A system (3.6) is irreducible provided that none of the variables can be solved for by solving less than n equations.) Furthermore, it transpires that some very important problems (in aerodynamics and in civil engineering, for example) yield large systems of linear equations possessing diagonally dominant determinants. Typically, it is not possible to provide accurate preliminary estimates for the unknowns x_i, and so these are often assigned the value zero initially as in Example 3–1.

Exercises

6. Draw a flowchart of the Gauss-Seidel method, and then write a computer program and solve:

$$A\ x_1 - 2x_2 + x_3 = 1$$
$$x_1 + Bx_2 + x_3 = 2$$
$$3x_1 - x_2 + Cx_3 = 1$$

where,

   a. $A = 4$, $B = 2$, $C = 4$
   b. $A = B = C = 10$
   c. $A = B = C = 100$.

Choose $N = 200$ and $\epsilon = 0.00001$. Which of these three cases do you expect to converge the fastest?

7. Is the Gauss-Seidel method guaranteed to solve the following system?

$$x_1 - 3x_2 + x_3 = -2$$
$$4x_1 + 2x_2 - x_3 = 1$$
$$x_1 \qquad + x_3 = 1$$

Solve these equations.

8. Perform the first five iterations of the Gauss-Seidel method on the system (3.1), starting with $x = y = 0$. Now trace these successive iterates on the graph in Figure 3a. Finally, interpret geometrically the sufficient condition for convergence in the case of two linear equations in two unknown variables.

9. Verify that the Gauss-Seidel method converges for the equations

$$x + 3y = 8$$
$$x - 4y = -10$$

even though the determinant is not diagonally dominant. Try to explain this behavior geometrically.

10. Calculate the unknown temperatures $x_1, x_2, ..., x_6$ that obey the following system of equations.

$$4x_1 - x_2 - x_3 \qquad\qquad\qquad = 2$$
$$-x_1 + 4x_2 \qquad - x_4 \qquad\qquad = 6$$
$$-x_1 \qquad + 4x_3 - x_4 - x_5 \qquad = 2$$
$$\quad - x_2 - x_3 + 4x_4 \qquad - x_6 = 5$$
$$\qquad\quad - x_3 \qquad + 4x_5 - x_6 = 8$$
$$\qquad\qquad\quad - x_4 - x_5 + 4x_6 = 12$$

Iterate using the Gauss-Seidel method with $\epsilon = 0.0001$.

3. Gaussian Elimination

Although the Gauss-Seidel method operates efficiently and is straightforward to program, it suffers from the disadvantage that convergence is guaranteed only for special versions of the general problem (3.6). A method that most of us met in high school provides, at least in theory, an alternative technique for solving all systems of the type (3.6). For large sets of equations this alternative method, which numerical analysts call Gaussian elimination, may be difficult to implement on a given computer because of storage restrictions (although the appearance of computing systems with virtual memories is very significant in this respect.) Also, for some problems, rounding errors can cause Gaussian elimination to produce values for the unknowns x_1, x_2,...,x_n which differ considerably from their true values.

In spite of these occasional drawbacks, Gaussian elimination is the technique most frequently used to solve sets of linear equations. We shall first review the method by solving a small problem as Example 3–2, and following this a flowchart is provided for implementing the general procedure on a computer.

Example 3–2. Using Gaussian elimination, solve the system

$$2x_1 + 2x_2 - 4x_3 = 4$$
$$x_1 - x_2 + 2x_3 = 4 \tag{3.8}$$
$$4x_1 - 2x_2 - 2x_3 = 20$$

The first stage of the method consists of eliminating x_1 from the second and third equations of (3.8). This is accomplished by first subtracting a suitable multiple of the first equation from the second equation, and then subtracting a suitable multiple of the first equation from the third equation. These multipliers are just the ratios of the coefficients of x_1 in each equation to the coefficient of x_1 in the first equation; in this case they are 1/2 and 2, respectively. Thus the system (3.8) is rewritten as

$$2x_1 + 2x_2 - 4x_3 = 4$$
$$- 2x_2 + 4x_3 = 2 \tag{3.9}$$
$$- 6x_2 + 6x_3 = 12$$

The second stage of the method eliminates x_2 from the third equation of (3.9). This involves only the second and third equations, and the necessary multiplier is $(-6)/(-2) = 3$. The original system (3.8) is then rewritten, via (3.9), as

$$2x_1 + 2x_2 - 4x_3 = 4$$
$$- 2x_2 + 4x_3 = 2 \tag{3.10}$$
$$- 6x_3 = 6$$

The motivation for the Gaussian elimination technique becomes clear upon inspection of the system (3.10): these arithmetic manipulations have reduced the equations (3.8) to an equivalent set (3.10) for which a solution can easily be found. Thus, the third equation of (3.10) yields

$$x_3 = 6/(-6) = -1,$$

the second equation then gives

$$x_2 = (2 - 4(-1))/(-2) = -3,$$

and finally, from the first equation we have that

$$x_1 = (4 + 4(-1) - 2(-3))/2 = 3.$$

The solution (x_1, x_2, x_3) to (3.8), obtained by back substitution on (3.10), is therefore $(3, -3, -1)$.

We can describe the Gaussian elimination method as a step by step triangularization of a given system of linear equations, followed by a back substitution as the final stage. An apparent pitfall for the method is the possible occurrence of a zero coefficient of the first variable in the first equation of the original system, or the second variable of the second equation at the next stage, and so on. More specifically, in Example 3–2 if either the coefficient of x_1 in the first equation of (3.8) is zero, or the coefficient of x_2 in the second equation of (3.9) is zero, how can we form the multipliers necessary for the eliminations? This problem can be avoided by simply interchanging (say) the first equation with any other equation for which the coefficient of x_1 is not zero, and repeating this process where necessary throughout the successive stages of the method. Provided that the original system has a unique solution, it is quite easy to prove that a satisfactory interchange is always feasible at each stage. Moreover, since any computer program for Gaussian elimination must include this safeguard feature, we shall insist that a row interchange be made at every stage to ensure that the coefficient with largest absolute value is always employed when forming the multipliers for that stage. Thus, in Example 3–2 the first and third equations of (3.8) should be interchanged so that the coefficient 4 is used to form the multipliers for the first stage. This minor modification improves the accuracy of the elimination method when it is implemented on a computer, since the overall effect of rounding errors can thereby be reduced for most problems.

A flowchart for the solution of the general system (3.6) by Gaussian elimination is contained in Figures 3b and 3c. We have omitted from Figure 3b the precise instructions that are required to implement the minor modification described above; this segment of the program is left as an exercise for the reader.

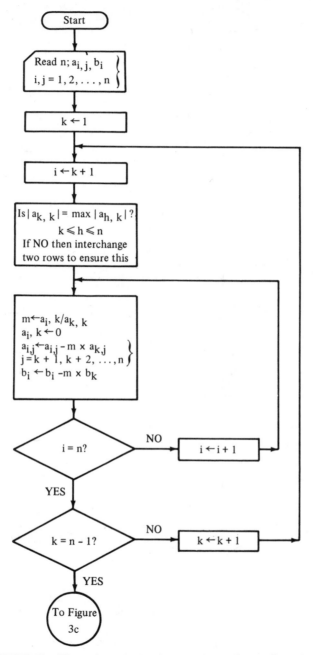

FIGURE 3b: The triangularization process of the Gaussian elimination method for solving a system of n linear equations.

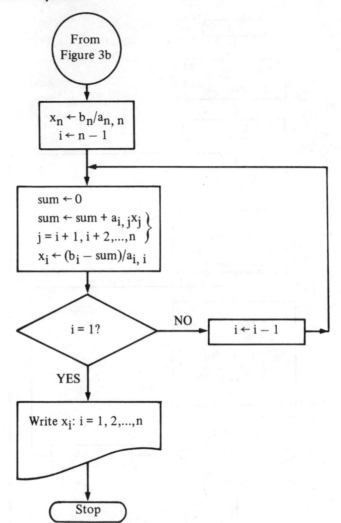

FIGURE 3c: The back substitution segment of Gaussian elimination.

Exercises

11. Write a computer program for Gaussian elimination, and use it to solve:

  a. Equations (3.1)
  b. Equations (3.2)

c. $x_1 + 5x_2 + 3x_3 - 3x_4 = 2$
$3x_1 + 19x_2 + 11x_3 - 12x_4 = 7$
$-x_1 + 8x_2 + 2x_3 - 5x_4 = 6$
$x_1 - 3x_2 \qquad + 4x_4 = -1$

d. $x_1 + x_2 + 2x_3 + 3x_4 = 13$
$x_1 + 2x_2 - x_3 + 9x_4 = 18$
$-2x_1 - 5x_2 + 6x_3 - 22x_4 = -40$
$-x_1 + 4x_2 - 15x_3 + 34x_4 = 13$

12. Solve the system

$$3x_1 + 11x_2 + 9x_3 = b_1$$
$$x_1 + 4x_2 + 2x_3 = b_2$$
$$2x_1 + 10x_2 + 8x_3 = b_3$$

where,

a. $b_1 = 12, b_2 = 3, b_3 = 10$
b. $b_1 = 21, b_2 = 3, b_3 = 20$
c. $b_1 = 2, b_2 = 3, b_3 = 4$.

Modify your Gaussian elimination program in order to avoid repeating the triangularization of this system.

13. Try to solve the following set of equations by Gaussian elimination.

$$x_1 - x_2 + x_3 = 1$$
$$5x_1 - 4x_2 + 3x_3 = 3$$
$$7x_1 - 6x_2 + 5x_3 = 2$$

What causes the trouble?

14. Solve the equations

$$13x + 17y = 10$$
$$10x + 13y = 1$$

using your Gaussian elimination program. Solve the system again after replacing the coefficient 17 by 16.95. Repeat both calculations in multiple precision. Any comments?

15. Try to estimate the range of solutions which satisfy the set of equations (3.1) when all the coefficients are considered to be in error by at most ± 0.1.

4. Least-Squares Estimation

A common problem in scientific computing is that of fitting a curve to a set of data points $[(x_1, y_1), (x_2, y_2),...,(x_m, y_m)]$. For example, each of the m data points (x_i, y_i) might correspond to a measurement y_i of the mass of a growing organism taken at time x_i. When plotted on a graph these observations could resemble those shown in Figure 3d. The biologist who conducted the experiment is interested in estimating the mass of the organism at some instants of time other than those at which measurements are available. He is also aware that all his measurements are subject to experimental error. He therefore wishes to approximate the shape of his data with a continuous curve, which will in some sense compensate for these experimental errors by not passing exactly through too many of the data points.

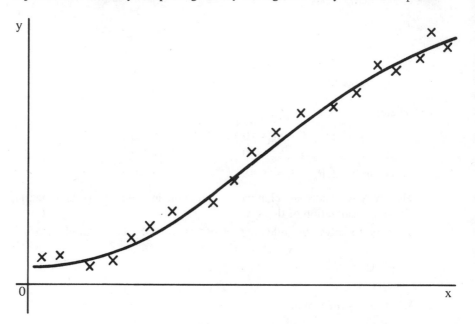

FIGURE 3d: A typical least-squares estimate for a set of data points.

The experimental curve in Figure 3d resembles the characteristic shape of a cubic polynomial $y = a_0 + a_1 x + a_2 x^2 + a_3 x^3$. The undetermined parameters a_0, a_1, a_2, and a_3 can be chosen so that the cubic polynomial approximates the data as closely as possible, in the least-squares sense. This is interpreted to mean that the parameters a_j are calculated to minimize the sum of squares S_3, where

$$S_3 = \sum_{i=1}^{m} \left\{ y_i - (a_0 + a_1 x_i + a_2 x_i^2 + a_3 x_i^3) \right\}^2 \tag{3.11}$$

(We use the subscript 3 on the left side of the equality (3.11) to indicate that the approximation is by a cubic polynomial.) From the differential calculus, we are assured that the unique minimum of S_3 occurs when all of the partial derivatives $\partial S_3 / \partial a_j = 0$. If we form these partial derivatives of (3.11), and rearrange the resulting equations, the following system of linear equations (3.12) results:

$$ma_0 + \left(\sum_{i=1}^{m} x_i\right) a_1 + \left(\sum_{i=1}^{m} x_i^2\right) a_2 + \left(\sum_{i=1}^{m} x_i^3\right) a_3 = \sum_{i=1}^{m} y_i$$

$$\left(\sum_{i=1}^{m} x_i\right) a_0 + \left(\sum_{i=1}^{m} x_i^2\right) a_1 + \left(\sum_{i=1}^{m} x_i^3\right) a_2 + \left(\sum_{i=1}^{m} x_i^4\right) a_3 = \sum_{i=1}^{m} x_i y_i$$

$$\left(\sum_{i=1}^{m} x_i^2\right) a_0 + \left(\sum_{i=1}^{m} x_i^3\right) a_1 + \left(\sum_{i=1}^{m} x_i^4\right) a_2 + \left(\sum_{i=1}^{m} x_i^5\right) a_3 = \sum_{i=1}^{m} x_i^2 y_i$$

$$\left(\sum_{i=1}^{m} x_i^3\right) a_0 + \left(\sum_{i=1}^{m} x_i^4\right) a_1 + \left(\sum_{i=1}^{m} x_i^5\right) a_2 + \left(\sum_{i=1}^{m} x_i^6\right) a_3 = \sum_{i=1}^{m} x_i^3 y_i$$

$$(3.12)$$

The system (3.12) of four linear equations in the four unknowns a_0, a_1, a_2, and a_3 can be solved by Gaussian elimination.

In practice, scientists often try to limit the use of the method of least-squares to polynomials of degree not exceeding six or seven. This is because the rounding errors incurred when calculating a least-squares polynomial of higher degree, in the above manner, will often cause values for the parameters to be produced which bear little resemblance to their true values. Thus this most useful application of the popular elimination technique also provides a striking example of one of the chief limitations of modern computers in scientific calculations.

Exercises

16. Calculate the least-squares cubic polynomial for the following data:

a.

x	0	1	2	3	4	5	6	7	8	9
y	8	9	13	13	12	10	7	6	6	8

b.

x	0	2	4	5	6	9	8	1
y	1.1	4.9	8.8	11.8	12.1	20.3	17.0	1.9

c.

x	0.1	0.2	0.3	0.4	1.0	3.0	10.0	20.0
y	1.0	0.9	0.7	0.6	1.0	1.7	3.1	4.5

Draw graphs of these estimates.

17. Calculate the least-squares cubic polynomial to e^x, by first generating

values for e^x when $x = 0, 0.1, 0.2,...,1.0$. What value does this cubic yield when $x = 0.75$? How well does this value compare to e^x when $x = 0.75$?

18. The least-squares polynomial of degree n can be calculated by solving a general system of linear equations for $a_0, a_1,...,a_n$. Equations (3.12) are just the particular case where $n = 3$. For example, when $n = 1$ the relevant system is obtained from the top-left corner of (3.12),

$$ma_0 + \left(\sum_{i=1}^{m} x_i\right) a_1 = \sum_{i=1}^{m} y_i$$

$$\left(\sum_{i=1}^{m} x_i\right) a_0 + \left(\sum_{i=1}^{m} x_i^2\right) a_1 = \sum_{i=1}^{m} x_i y_i.$$

Calculate the least-squares polynomial, for $n=1$ and $n=2$, to the data in Exercise 16a.

19. The average price of one share of a certain computer manufacturing company has varied as shown:

Year	1962	1963	1964	1965	1966	1967	1968	1969	1970
Price	$52	$73	$89	$120	$190	$230	$290	$350	$360

Estimate the average price in 1971 and 1972 based on the least-squares straight line for this data. How useful are these estimates likely to be?

20. Calculate the least-squares polynomial for $n = 2, 4, 6, 8, 10$, and 12, to the data:

x	0	1	2	3	4	5	6	7	8	9	10	11	12	13	14	15
y	0.0	1.0	1.4	1.7	2.0	2.1	2.2	2.3	2.5	2.9	3.0	3.1	3.2	3.2	3.3	3.3

Observe the initial steady decrease in the sum of squares S_n, and the correlation between the coefficients of the various polynomials. What causes the erratic behavior of the output from your Gaussian elimination program for the larger values of n? Repeat the calculations in multiple precision.

5. Summary

In this chapter we have been dealing with one of the most frequently encountered problems in computing. The computer solution of a system of linear equations can nowadays be regarded as an almost routine task, and most computing centres have at least one standard program available for this purpose. Although in view of their large size or condition, some practical problems will always require special attention from an experienced scientific programmer.

For a diagonally dominant sparse system (i.e. one which contains a relatively large number of zero coefficients) the Gauss-Seidel method allows us to compute a solution even when the number of equations runs into the tens of thousands. Essentially, this is because this iterative method can operate with just the original elements a_{ij} which are nonzero; the zero elements need not even be stored. In practice, sparse linear equation systems with over 100,000 unknowns have been solved successfully.

To date, the general use of the Gaussian elimination method has been restricted to much smaller sets of equations. Even if the system originally contains a large number of zero elements, the triangularization stage of Gaussian elimination tends to change these elements to nonzero values which must be stored. However, the Gaussian elimination technique can deal with many different types of linear systems of equations, and it always produces a computer solution which is the exact solution to a slight perturbation of the problem at hand. Also, rather sophisticated error analyses can be made via this method for the frequent cases where the coefficients of the equations are known to be in error.

The method of least-squares is very important in data analysis. It is discussed further in Chapter 7, and an alternative method for approximating data is developed in Chapter 6.

Exercises

21. Solve Exercise 6 and Exercise 10 using Gaussian elimination.

22. Solve graphically the system of linear equations

$$3x + 6y = 9, \qquad 3x + 6.00001y = 9.00001 ;$$

and also the system

$$3x + 6y = 9, \qquad 3x + 5.99999y = 9.00002.$$

Also solve both systems using your Gaussian elimination program. Repeat these computer calculations in multiple precision.

23. Suppose that you have computed the solution to a system of linear equations numerically, but you suspect that the computed solution differs considerably from the exact solution. Substituting the computed solution into each equation of the system yields numbers which agree closely with the constants on the right-hand side. Can you then be sure that the computed solution is accurate? Exercise 22 should help in answering this question correctly.

24. Solve the system

$$-3.7361x_1 + 1.4998x_2 + 7.6228x_3 + 1.0021x_4 = 5.9972$$
$$1.8666x_1 - 1.1104x_2 + 1.2460x_3 + 8.3982x_4 = 4.0031$$
$$8.4375x_1 + 2.1183x_2 - 3.7472x_3 + 1.8821x_4 = 4.6391$$
$$2.1356x_1 + 5.7721x_2 + 1.4213x_3 - 1.1231x_4 = 4.9998$$

25. Generalize the Gauss-Seidel iterative technique in order to solve the following nonlinear system of equations:

$$x_1 - 0.1x_2{}^2 + 0.05x_3{}^2 = 0.1$$
$$x_2 + 0.3x_1{}^2 - 0.1x_1x_3 = 1.0$$
$$x_3 + 0.4x_2{}^2 + 0.1x_1x_2 = 2.4$$

26. Find all the solutions of

$$x_1 + 2x_2 + 3x_3 + 4x_4 = 5$$
$$2x_1 - x_2 + x_3 - x_4 = 1$$
$$3x_1 + x_2 + 4x_3 + 3x_4 = 6$$
$$-2x_1 + 6x_2 + 4x_3 + 10x_4 = 8$$

27. A patient recovering from a long illness requires one meal per day containing 11 units of vitamin A, 9 of vitamin B, and 20 of vitamin C. Food 1 has 1 unit of vitamin A, 3 units of vitamin B, and 4 units of vitamin C. Food 2 has 2, 3, and 5 units of vitamins A, B, and C, respectively. Finally, Food 3 has 3 units each of vitamins A and B, but none of vitamin C.

a. Find all combinations of Foods 1, 2, and 3 that will provide precisely the required amounts of each vitamin.

b. If Food 1 costs $1 and the others cost 50 cents each per unit, is there a combination that costs exactly $2? Which combination costs the least amount?

28. A certain sum of money is divided among A, B, and C. B's share is 50 cents more than half the sum of the shares of A and C. A's share is $4 less than half the sum of the shares of B and C. If the shares of A and B together amount to $33, find how much each receives.

29. There is a number whose three digits, from left to right, are in descending order of magnitude and differ from each other in succession by the same amount. If the number is divided by the sum of its digits the quotient is 48; and if 198 is subtracted from the number the difference is equal to the number obtained by reversing the digits of the original number. Find the original number. (Do not waste valuable computing time on this problem!)

30. Calculate a "good approximation" by a low degree polynomial to the following empirical function:

x	0	$\frac{\pi}{12}$	$\frac{2\pi}{12}$	$\frac{3\pi}{12}$	$\frac{4\pi}{12}$	$\frac{5\pi}{12}$	$\frac{6\pi}{12}$	$\frac{7\pi}{12}$	$\frac{8\pi}{12}$	$\frac{9\pi}{12}$	$\frac{10\pi}{12}$	$\frac{11\pi}{12}$	π
f(x)	0	0.21	0.37	0.54	0.71	0.85	0.94	0.99	1.01	0.98	0.86	0.51	0

(Although the instructions in this exercise are rather vague, they are also quite typical of requests made in practice! Assume that the experimentalist requires this approximation in order to estimate f(x) for values of x not tabulated.)

31. The temperature distribution inside a square pipe obeys Laplace's equation. The outside of the pipe is at varying temperatures, as indicated in the cross-section shown, and it is required to find the temperatures $x_1, x_2, ..., x_{15}$ at uniformly spaced interior points of the pipe.

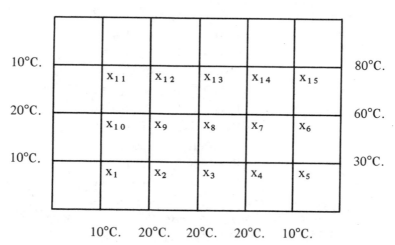

Assuming that the temperature at an interior point is equal to the average of the temperatures at its four neighbouring points (to the North, South, East, and West), calculate these unknown temperatures using the Gauss-Seidel iterative method. (Hint: The resulting set of linear equations should resemble the structure of the system given in Exercise 10.)

32. For the electrical network shown below, Kirchhoff's laws may be used to establish the following set of linear equations.

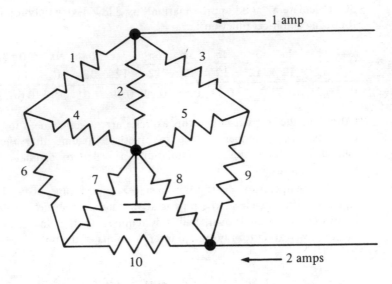

$$
\begin{aligned}
I_1 + I_2 + I_3 &= 1 \\
I_8 + I_9 + I_{10} &= 2 \\
-I_1 + I_4 - I_6 &= 0 \\
-I_3 + I_5 - I_9 &= 0 \\
I_6 + I_7 - I_{10} &= 0 \\
-R_7 I_7 + R_8 I_8 - R_{10} I_{10} &= 0 \\
-R_5 I_5 + R_8 I_8 - R_9 I_9 &= 0 \\
R_2 I_2 - R_3 I_3 - R_5 I_5 &= 0 \\
-R_1 I_1 + R_2 I_2 - R_4 I_4 &= 0 \\
-R_4 I_4 - R_6 I_6 + R_7 I_7 &= 0
\end{aligned}
$$

Solve this system for the unknown currents I_1, I_2,...,I_{10}, when the resistances (in ohms) are $R_1 = R_2 = R_4 = 7$, $R_3 = R_5 = 2$, $R_6 = 4$, $R_7 = 5$, $R_8 = R_{10} = 4$, $R_9 = 8$.

33. Find out about:

    a. matrices;

    b. matrix inversion;

    c. least-squares estimation by functions other than polynomials.

34. In the book by Forsythe and Moler referred to below, there are computer programs in FORTRAN, PL/1, and ALGOL for Gaussian elimination. Solve any of the systems of linear equations of the previous exercises using one of these programs.

Further Reading

Forsythe, G. E. and C. B. Moler, *Computer Solution of Linear Algebraic Systems,* Prentice-Hall, 1967.

Froberg, C. E., *Introduction to Numerical Analysis,* 2nd Ed., Addison-Wesley, Reading, Mass., 1969.

Householder, A. S., *Principles of Numerical Analysis,* McGraw-Hill, New York, 1953.

McCracken, D. D. and W. S. Dorn, *Numerical Methods and FORTRAN Programming,* John Wiley, New York, 1964.

Ralston, A., *A First Course in Numerical Analysis,* McGraw-Hill, New York, 1965.

B

Operations Research

What is operations research?

Operations Research is the application of scientific techniques in the study of industrial, military and governmental processes. The first uses of Operations Research were in World War II, where military activities such as bombing missions, mining operations, submarine search patterns and the structuring of convoys were first analyzed scientifically. In the early 1950's, the techniques of Operations Research were extended and applied to industry and government. This expansion in Operations Research was stimulated by the advent of the second industrial revolution and the development of the electronic computer. In Britain, the nationalization of the coal, steel, and rail industries created opportunities for the early workers in this field. In the United States, industrial concerns used the techniques of Operations Research to reduce costs, increase production, and to speed transportation of their products to the consumers.

Modern Operations Research techniques include simulation, linear programming, statistics, inventory control, queueing theory, game theory, network analysis, transportation problems, job scheduling, and personnel assignment. One of the more difficult tasks facing the worker in Operations Research is to identify the problem at hand, to describe it mathematically, and then to select the appropriate technique for its solution. Of the techniques listed, the first three are the most commonly used, and hence we have chosen to present them here. We also include ample discussion of how these techniques can be implemented on a computer.

Finally, we note that a thorough presentation of linear programming at this level is difficult. However, in view of the importance of the topic, we have included an elementary discussion of this powerful technique. The simplex method, which is used to solve linear programming problems, is described in detail, and we include some discussion on the mathematical theory of this technique.

There is no doubt that Operations Research will continue to expand and become more diverse in the future, and we hope that our presentation will encourage the reader to do some further reading in this area.

4

Deterministic Simulation

1. Introduction

Simulation is the technique of imitating a physical process. Examples of processes which we may wish to simulate are the motion of a rocket, the arrival of cars at an intersection, the arrival of telephone calls at a telephone exchange, the motion of a neutron through the wall of an atomic reactor, the processing of jobs on a computer. Having obtained a working simulation of a physical process, it is usually quite easy to alter various parameters of the model, and observe how it operates with these changes. For example we may wish to change the thickness of the wall of an atomic reactor, or alter the phasing of the traffic lights at an intersection, or change the fuel mass carried by a rocket. Experimenting with a computer simulation of a physical process is usually much faster, easier and cheaper than experimenting with the process itself. In this and the following chapter we shall consider various processes which may be simulated within a computer.

The first stage in the design of a simulation is to make a mathematical model of the process. Two types of models can be used to describe a process; a deterministic model or a probabilistic model. Newton's law of motion

$$f = m \times a \qquad (4.1)$$

is a mathematical model which governs the motion of an object of mass m acted on by a force f. This model is deterministic in that the acceleration a produced by the force is defined by the equation. If an object is thrown vertically with initially velocity u, the distance s travelled in time t is given by

$$s = ut - \frac{1}{2} gt^2 \qquad (4.2)$$

where g is the acceleration due to gravity.

Both equations (4.1) and (4.2) are deterministic models in the sense that they predict the state of the physical process. However, it is not always possible to make such a model of a physical process. Consider the simple operation of flipping a coin. Although Newtonian mechanics should predict whether the coin lands heads or tails, (given the initial velocity, spin, height, etc.) in practice it is impossible to determine this in advance. Hence a deterministic model cannot be used. We may observe that in a large number of trials, approximately half the time the coin lands heads, and half the time tails. We can make a probabilistic model of this process by saying that the probability that the coin lands heads equals a half. Mathematically, our model of the process can be written

$$p(H) = \frac{1}{2} , \; p(T) = \frac{1}{2} .$$

Although this probabilistic model cannot be used to determine precisely what will happen, much useful information can be gained about the physical process by studying such a model. Rolling dice or spinning a roulette wheel are other physical processes where a probabilistic model is appropriate.

Given a model of either type, it often happens that the mathematical formulation is difficult or even impossible to solve in practice. It is possible, however, to obtain approximate solutions to the problem by simulating the physical process within a computer. The process of simulation is a very powerful method of obtaining approximate solutions to otherwise intractable problems. The examples which follow, although fairly simple, serve to demonstrate the basic techniques of simulation. In the remainder of this chapter we discuss deterministic simulation, while the following chapter is concerned with probabilistic simulation.

2. The Missile Attack Problem

An aircraft is being attacked by a missile which contains a homing device. At any instant of time, the missile is programmed to head directly for the aircraft. The problem is to determine the path of the missile and also to determine how long before the collision occurs. For simplicity we assume the aircraft is flying horizontally and the missile is in the same horizontal plane as the aircraft. The missile initially heads directly at the aircraft, but since the aircraft is moving, the missile changes direction continuously so that it is always pointing towards the aircraft. If the path of the aircraft is curved, a deterministic mathematical model of this process is difficult or even impossible to solve. For the case under consideration, the problem is mathematically tractable although its solution is by no means trivial. We can obtain an approximate solution to the problem by simulating the motion of both the aircraft and the missile on a computer.

We assume that the aircraft is initially at the origin (0, 0), but is moving along the x axis with velocity 500 feet/second (see Figure 4a). The missile is initially at the point with coordinates (40000, 100000) and moving at 1000 feet/second. To simulate the process we select a small time interval and consider the motion at discrete time steps. For this problem a time interval of 1 second is chosen. Suppose the simulation has been conducted for time t. We wish to determine the positions of the aircraft and the missile at time t + 1. In Figure 4b we denote the horizontal distance moved in time t by the aircraft by d, and the coordinates of the missile by (x, y).

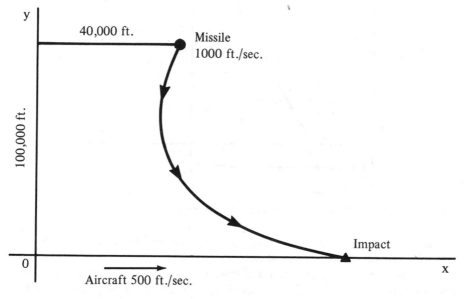

FIGURE 4a: The missile attack problem.

The distance between the aircraft and missile can be computed using the well-known theorem of Pythagoras, and is given by

$$s = \sqrt{y^2 + (x-d)^2}$$

The direction θ in which the missile heads is determined by

$$\sin \theta = (x - d)/s \, , \, \cos \theta = y/s$$

For each 1 second interval, the coordinates of the missile are changed to

$$x \leftarrow x - 1000 \sin \theta \ , \ y \leftarrow y - 1000 \cos \theta \ ,$$
$$\text{i.e.} \ \ x \leftarrow x - 1000 \times (x{-}d)/s \ , \ y \leftarrow y - 1000 \times y/s \ .$$

The position of the aircraft is changed to

$$d \leftarrow d + 500 \ .$$

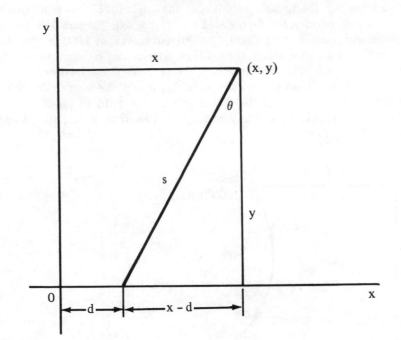

FIGURE 4b: Position of aircraft and missile at time t.

A flowchart for the computer simulation is given in Figure 4c. Note that we terminate the simulation when $s < 500$.

The output from the simulation will be the coordinates (x, y) of the missile and the distance d travelled by the aircraft at 1 second intervals. Thus it is possible to plot the path of the missile fairly accurately. Since a 1 second time interval may not be small enough for the accuracy we require, it is a good idea to run the simulation again using 1/2 second or even 1/10 second intervals. Finally we note that the simulation technique can be extended to 3-dimensions and also allow for evasive action on the part of the aircraft.

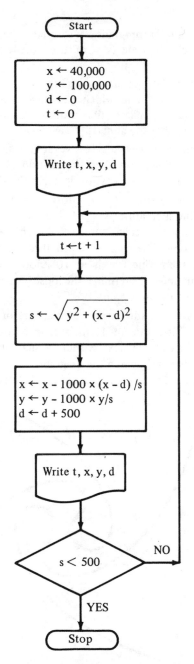

FIGURE 4c: Simulation of a missile attack.

Exercises

1. Write a computer program to simulate the missile attack problem. Plot a graph of the trajectory of the missile and determine the time until collision.

2. Suppose that the aircraft carries its own missile which can travel at 800 feet per second, and which contains a device for homing on an attacking missile. Simulate the motion of the aircraft and the two missiles assuming that the aircraft releases its missile after 40 seconds.

3. Suppose the aircraft takes evasive action and flies at right angles to the path of the missile. Simulate the motion of both aircraft and missile. Does this evasive action increase or decrease the time until impact?

4. A ship is travelling at 20 knots and is heading directly for a submarine. The submarine is sighted at a distance of 5 nautical miles. The ship's captain decides to turn the ship around and head in the opposite direction. The ship can turn through an angle of 1 degree in 6 seconds. The submarine travels at 10 knots and heads directly towards the ship at all times. Determine the positions of both the ship and the submarine at their closest point.

5. Four snails are at the corners of a square of size 100 cms. Each snail starts to crawl at a rate of 1 cm./sec. in a counter clockwise direction towards the snail at the next corner. A snail always aims directly at the snail he is chasing as shown in the diagram.

The snails eventually meet in the centre of the square. Simulate the motion of the snails and determine the time until they meet. Plot a graph of the paths of the snails. Use a 1 second time interval for your simulation. Repeat the simulation using 1/2 second and 1/5 second time intervals. Why are the answers different? Can you solve the problem analytically?

3. Motion of a Rocket

As a second example of a deterministic simulation we consider the motion of a rocket. This motion is determined by the laws of Newtonian mechanics. In a practical situation, these laws when expressed as a mathematical model are usually impossible to solve by standard mathematical techniques. We can, however, simulate the motion of the rocket on a computer and thus observe how the rocket performs under differing conditions. Before considering such a complicated model, we shall first discuss a simpler situation and see how a simulation can be developed.

We consider an object of mass m, initially at rest, acted on by a force f. The force produces an acceleration a, and the mathematical model of this system is given by Newton's law of motion (4.1). The acceleration produced by the force is thus a constant equal to f/m. We are interested in evaluating the velocity and distance travelled at any given time. This particular problem can be solved quite easily using standard mathematical techniques. To simulate the motion we consider small time intervals of length tstep. Assume that the simulation has proceeded for several time intervals, and that at time t the velocity is v and the distance travelled x. We wish to evaluate the new velocity and new distance at the end of the next time interval, t + tstep. Since by definition, acceleration is rate of change of velocity, the velocity at time t + tstep is given by

$$v \leftarrow v + a \times tstep. \tag{4.3}$$

Similarly, since velocity is rate of change of distance, the distance travelled at time t + tstep is given by

$$x \leftarrow x + v \times tstep. \tag{4.4}$$

The velocity used in equation (4.4) may be either the velocity at time t, or the velocity at time t + tstep. In practice the time step is chosen sufficiently small for the difference to be negligible, and we shall adopt the convention that the velocity is always altered before the distance. Essentially we have discretized a continuous process, which means that our simulation model is only an approximation to the physical process. The smaller we choose tstep, the better our approximation will be. However, too small a value of tstep can cause numerical problems (this situation is analogous to that depicted in Figure 2d). A

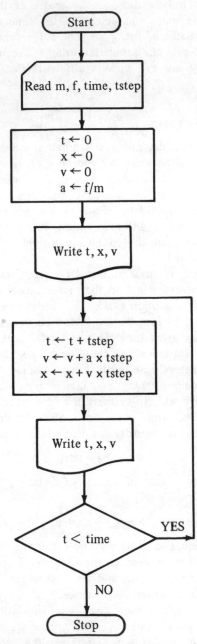

FIGURE 4d: Simulation of the motion of an object of constant mass acted on by a constant force.

flowchart of the simulation is given in Figure 4d. We terminate the simulation when the time t is greater than a given time which we input initially.

We now consider the more difficult problem of simulating the motion of a rocket. We shall consider a rocket which is propelled by the combustion of fuel. One of the difficulties of analyzing such a problem mathematically is that the mass of the rocket is being continually reduced. We shall simulate the motion of the rocket until all the fuel is burned, and then continue the simulation as the rocket returns to earth under gravity. We start the simulation with the rocket on the launch pad. We shall consider a rocket with mass m = 5000 lbs., and fuel mass fm = 5000 lbs. The initial total mass tm = 10000 lbs. Fuel is used at a constant rate r = 50 lbs/sec. causing a thrust f = 400,000 ft. lbs./sec./sec. The rocket is aimed vertically for 10 seconds and is thereafter inclined at an angle θ = 20 degrees to the vertical. We shall assume that the acceleration due to gravity is a constant g = 32 ft./sec./sec. As fuel is burned in the rocket, the total mass tm decreases from its initial value of 10,000 lbs. at a rate of 50 lbs./sec. for 100 seconds. At this point the thrust is reduced to zero, and the rocket returns to earth. A typical path of the rocket is shown in Figure 4e.

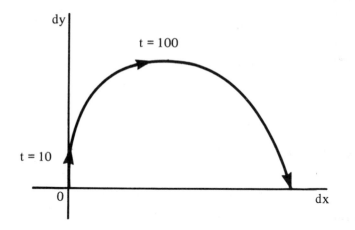

FIGURE 4e: Trajectory of a rocket.

To simulate the motion of the rocket we first make a deterministic model of the process. We set up coordinate axes as shown in Figure 4f. We denote the horizontal distance, velocity and acceleration by dx, vx, ax, and the vertical components by dy, vy, ay. The forces acting on the rocket are gravity and the thrust f. The force due to gravity acts vertically downwards and is of magnitude tm x g. The thrust f is initially vertical, is then inclined at an angle of θ degrees until all the fuel is burned, and is finally reduced to zero leaving only the gravitational force. We select a time step of one second. For each time interval, we wish to determine the change in acceleration velocity and distance components. We first decrease the total mass tm by 50 lbs. In the vertical direction there are two forces acting. The force due to gravity acts vertically downwards and is of magnitude tm × g. The vertical component of the thrust is f × cos θ. Thus the total vertical force is given by

$$f \times \cos \theta - tm \times g .$$

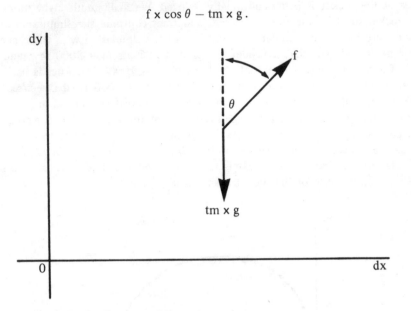

FIGURE 4f: Forces acting on the rocket.

Using Newton's law (4.1), the component of acceleration in the vertical direction is given by

$$ay \leftarrow (f \times \cos \theta - tm \times g)/tm$$

The velocity in the vertical direction is then changed to

$$vy \leftarrow vy + ay$$

and the vertical distance becomes

$$dy \leftarrow dy + vy$$

Note that if we use a time step different from one second, we must include this in the above two equations.

In the horizontal direction, the gravitational force has no effect, and hence the only force is the horizontal component of the thrust which is f × sin θ. Note that $\theta = 0$ for the first 10 seconds, and hence this force is of size zero. The horizontal components of acceleration, velocity and distance become

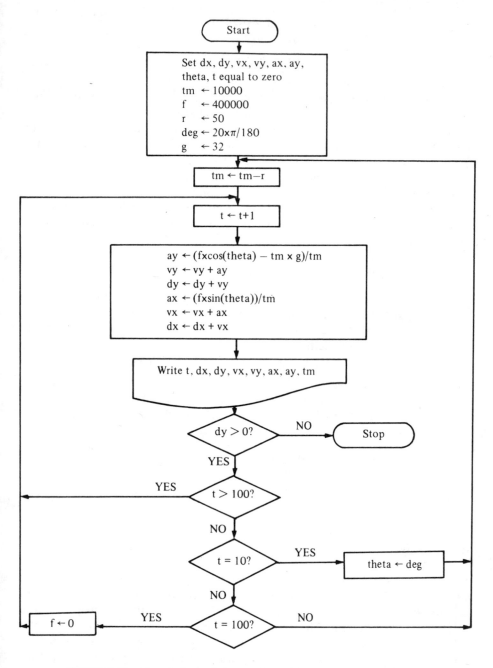

FIGURE 4g: Simulation of the motion of a rocket.

$$ax \leftarrow f \times \sin(\theta)/tm$$
$$vx \leftarrow vx + ax$$
$$dx \leftarrow dx + vx$$

A flowchart of the simulation is given in Figure 4g.

Our model does not take into account forces due to air resistance. In practice these forces are not negligible and must be included. One possible model is to assume that air resistance is proportional to the square of the velocity v. If the constant of proportionality is k, then the air resistance can be represented by a force $k\ v^2\ \sin(\alpha)$ in the direction of negative x, and $k\ v^2\ \cos(\alpha)$ in the direction of negative y, where α is the inclination of the direction of the motion of the rocket to the vertical. These can easily be incorporated into our simulation.

Finally, it may be that a 1 second time interval is not sufficiently small for the accuracy we require. Hence we may wish to repeat the simulation with a smaller time interval.

Exercises

6. Write a computer program to simulate the motion of the rocket. Plot a graph of the trajectory of the rocket and determine the position of the rocket when all the fuel is burned, and also the point at which the rocket returns to earth.

7. Repeat the simulation of the rocket assuming that air resistance forces are of magnitude $0.1v^2$ where v is the velocity of the rocket.

8. A rocket is fired from the surface of the earth in a vertical direction at an initial speed of 5 miles/sec. The gravitational attraction of the earth at a distance d miles from its surface is given by

$$g = \left\{ \frac{4000}{d+4000} \right\}^2 \times \frac{32}{5280} \ \text{miles/sec./sec.}$$

Simulate the motion of the rocket and determine whether it escapes from the earth.

4. Summary

Deterministic simulation is concerned with the simulation of a process for which we can make a deterministic model. If the mathematical model cannot be solved analytically, then a computer simulation can be used to produce an approximate solution to the problem. The mathematical model is usually in the form of a differential equation, and the deterministic simulation approach is essentially a numerical method for solving this equation. There do exist more accurate numerical techniques for solving differential equations, and the interested reader is referred to one of the standard textbooks on numerical analysis or differential equations.

Exercises

9. A baseball player hits a ball with initial velocity 130 ft./sec. at an angle of 30 degrees to the horizontal. At impact, the ball is 4 feet from the ground, and is aimed at a the centre field boundary fence which is 10 feet high and 400 feet away. Simulate the motion of the ball and determine if the player scores a home run.

10. A ball is thrown at an angle of 45° to the vertical with initial velocity 30 ft./sec. When the ball hits the ground it bounces, and at each bounce its horizontal component of velocity is unchanged, but its vertical component of velocity is reversed, and reduced to 90% of its previous value. Simulate the motion of the ball for the first ten bounces, and plot a graph of its trajectory. Use a time step of one-tenth of a second. Repeat the simulation using a time step of one-hundredth of a second.

11. A car weighing 2000 lbs. is travelling at 88 ft./sec.(= 60 miles/hour) when it reaches an incline of 10 degrees. The force produced by the engine of the car is inversely proportional to the velocity, and is given by

$$F = \frac{400,000}{v} \quad \text{ft.lbs./sec./sec.}$$

Simulate the motion of the car as it climbs the incline, and determine its terminal velocity.

12. A car weighing 2000 lbs. is travelling at 30 ft./sec. The force F produced by the engine is given by

$$F = \frac{400,000}{v} \text{ ft.lbs./sec./sec.}$$

where v is the velocity of the car. The force produced by air resistance is 0.4 v^2 ft.lbs./sec./sec. Simulate the motion of the car as it accelerates to its maximum velocity.

13. Repeat the simulation of Exercise 12 with

    a. the car climbing an incline of 10 degrees

    b. the car descending an incline of 10 degrees.

14. A pendulum consists of a string of length 100 inches with a weight attached. The pendulum is initially held horizontally. Simulate the motion of the pendulum until it reaches the vertical position.

15. A ring slides freely on the parabola $y = x^2$, and is initially at rest at the point with coordinates $(1, 1)$. Simulate the motion of the ring until it reaches the origin.

16. A tank contains 200 gallons of water in which 100 pounds of salt are dissolved. Suppose that water containing 2 pounds per gallon of salt runs into the tank at the rate of 6 gallons per minute, and that the mixture, kept uniform by stirring, runs out of the tank at the rate of 4 gallons per minute. Simulate this process and determine the amount of salt in the tank after 30 minutes.

17. Write a computer program to plot the curve which passes through the point with coordinates $(0, 1)$, and is such that at each point, the tangent line is perpendicular to the line joining the point to the origin.

18. Write a computer program to plot the curve which passes through the point with coordinates $(1, 0)$, and is such that the slope is equal to the reciprocal of the x coordinate.

19. A spring is fixed at its upper end and is hanging vertically with a 1 lb. weight attached. In its equilibrium position, the spring is of length 2 feet. The weight is set in motion by extending the spring a further 1 foot. Simulate the motion of the weight assuming that when it is displaced a distance x feet from its equilibrium position, there is a net force of magnitude 4x ft.lbs./sec./sec. acting on it. Determine the period of oscillation of the spring and plot a graph of the displacement against time. Use 1/100th second time interval for your simulation.

Further Reading

Gordon, G., *System Simulation,* Prentice-Hall, New Jersey, 1969.

Rice, J. K. and J. R. Rice. *Introduction to Computer Science,* Holt, Rinehart and Winston, New York, 1969.

Probabilistic Simulation

1. Introduction

In probabilistic simulation, we are concerned with simulating processes which can be described by a probabilistic model. Typical processes for which a probabilistic model is appropriate are the diffusion of neutrons through the lead wall of an atomic reactor, the flow of traffic through an intersection, a line of people waiting at a bus stop, and the arrival of telephone calls at an exchange. It is impossible to make a deterministic model of such processes. We cannot determine, for example, precisely when a telephone call will occur at a telephone exchange, or when a car will arrive at an intersection. However, it may be possible to describe these processes in terms of probabilities. We may observe that calls appear to arrive at a telephone exchange at random instants of time. By taking a small time interval, we can estimate the probability that a call occurs in this time interval. In the case of the motion of a neutron, its direction after a collision with an atom of lead may only be known with certain probabilities. To simulate these physical processes we must be able to simulate the randomness of these events. This is done by using a table of random numbers, or, if the simulation is being done within a computer, by using a random number generator. The examples which follow serve to demonstrate the basic techniques of probabilistic simulation.

77

2. A Simple Queueing Problem

The operation of a gas station is a typical example of a queueing (or waiting line) process. Although the particular problem we shall consider can be solved analytically by the mathematical techniques of queueing theory, we shall use this example to demonstrate how a simulation model can be constructed.

Cars arrive at a gas station at random, at an average rate of 20 per hour. The gas station has two pumps, and if both are occupied the arriving cars form a single queue or waiting line. Service is assumed to take exactly five minutes per car. We wish to find the average queue length, and the average time a car spends in the gas station.

To make a probabilistic model of this process we choose a small time interval; in this case a 1 minute interval is appropriate. Our model of the arrival pattern can be stated as follows:

$$\text{The probability that 1 arrival occurs in a 1 minute interval} = 1/3 \qquad (5.1)$$

$$\text{The probability that no arrivals occur in a 1 minute interval} = 2/3 \qquad (5.2)$$

On average, therefore, we expect 20 cars to arrive each hour. Note that we do not allow for more than one arrival in a one minute interval. If we wish to make our model more realistic, we can reduce the time interval to 1 second, or even 1/100 second. There are no definite rules for determining an appropriate time interval in general. It must be small enough for a reasonable mathematical model to be constructed, but large enough so that the simulation does not require a large amount of computer time. In fact, in the mathematical theory of queues we typically divide a finite time period into arbitrarily small time intervals. For our purposes, however, we shall consider the model given by equations (5.1) and (5.2).

To simulate the randomness of the events we require a table of random numbers. Table 5a contains a sequence of 1000 random digits. The probability that a particular digit occurs is 1/10.

We group the digits of the table together in fives, thus producing the sequence of random numbers

.39868   .42197   .26937   .08423   .82778   ...

Note that when we refer to a random number, we mean a number selected at random from the interval (0, 1). Although in theory such a number should have an infinite number of digits, it is usually sufficient to consider only the first few digits for simulation purposes.

Corresponding to each 1 minute interval we select the next random number in sequence. If the random number is less than .33333 then a car arrives at the gas station. For convenience we shall assume that the car arrives at the end of the time interval. If the random number is greater than or equal to .33333 then no

Table 5a: 1000 random digits.

39868	42197	26937	08423	82778	54275	17406	06051	94256	54219
22352	28994	74291	58183	61681	80374	35140	18159	32773	27085
44877	65180	18145	45747	81389	08432	36411	04986	84361	46221
00511	33418	02415	63804	31315	27986	10543	98478	83755	83935
65107	01340	20557	28373	24862	74755	89323	53914	33642	71345
69243	81716	26399	27321	63512	31920	46574	43990	61001	62727
36591	34093	44100	82653	20408	17986	36605	48414	27924	96190
71040	27013	13767	52647	69438	74309	60497	80854	59726	03932
50479	31885	33591	23279	26647	84597	02557	49162	46983	41064
20244	42636	80658	56642	19738	80967	47522	65735	24243	56420
42191	00134	77527	35140	83164	40207	24872	59533	56482	34830
65628	51973	02402	97955	54373	42457	95211	08154	10465	62596
71048	73652	56376	30470	02920	89838	81614	43002	53702	37263
03525	53806	89429	11799	76086	66757	16993	74180	17035	64027
31861	42107	80865	28987	93368	30377	88505	85467	09115	48334
87855	23843	13990	68699	90052	81690	87526	97232	20984	56587
84762	43254	45577	82367	57735	99752	26618	58872	38090	92853
86512	18703	13746	07479	83922	62661	31846	67670	27650	80485
04377	85977	52149	34337	23899	04285	68354	09317	95333	85999
91871	61436	90083	28781	13311	24167	34092	81992	84033	75128

car arrives in that time interval. Thus in the first two minutes no cars arrive, corresponding to random numbers .39868, .42197. In the third minute the random number .26937 is less than .33333 and hence a car arrives. If we start the simulation with the gas station empty, then car number 1 drives immediately to pump 1 where service commences. In the fourth minute, car number 2 arrives and drives immediately to pump 2. Table 5b describes the simulation of the gas station for 30 minutes.

We see from Table 5b that in 30 minutes 12 cars arrived at the gas station, of which 10 completed service. We can compute various statistics from the simulation. For example, the average queue length is $13/30 \simeq 0.43$, and the average total time in the system for the 10 cars which completed service is $60/10 = 6$ minutes. Clearly, these statistics depend upon the random numbers used. In practice we run the simulation on a computer for a much longer period of time, and then these statistics become virtually independent of the actual sequence of random numbers used. Techniques for generating random numbers within a computer were referred to previously in Chapter 2. Most computing installations have a standard subprogram available which generates random numbers.

Table 5b: Simulation of a gas station for 30 minutes.

Time	Pump 1	Pump 2	Queue	Time	Pump 1	Pump 2	Queue
1	0	0	0	16	5	6	0
2	0	0	0	17	5	6	0
3	1	0	0	18	7	6	0
4	1	2	0	19	7	8	0
5	1	2	0	20	7	8	9
6	1	2	0	21	7	8	9
7	1	2	3	22	7	8	9
8	3	2	4	23	9	8	10
9	3	4	0	24	9	10	0
10	3	4	0	25	9	10	0
11	3	4	5	26	9	10	11
12	3	4	5,6	27	9	10	11
13	5	4	6	28	11	10	12
14	5	6	0	29	11	12	0
15	5	6	0	30	11	12	0

Finally we note that it is a relatively simple matter to repeat the simulation with three gas pumps, and to compute the average service time and average queue length with this change in the system. It is usually much easier to alter parameters in a simulation model than to make changes in the actual physical process. This is one of the major reasons for using simulation techniques.

Exercises

1. Run the simulation of the gas station for a 60 minute period using a different sequence of random numbers. Compute the average queue length and the average total time a car spends in the system.

2. Repeat the simulation of the gas station assuming that there are three pumps and that the arrival rate increases to 30 cars per hour.

3. Use the random numbers in Table 5a to simulate the following processes:

   a. the rolling of two dice;

   b. the spinning of a roulette wheel.

(Hint: Suppose the roulette wheel contains 36 numbers 1–36. Group the digits of the table in fives to produce random numbers between 0 and 1. Multiply each number by 36 and add 1; this produces random numbers between 1 and 37. Ignoring the fractional parts of these numbers produces a sequence of random integers corresponding to the numbers 1−36 on the roulette wheel.)

3. Neutron Diffusion

One of the earliest applications of simulation was in the design of atomic reactors. A simplification of the original problem will serve to demonstrate the basic techniques used.*

The wall of an atomic reactor is made of lead. Neutrons enter the wall from inside the reactor and collide with atoms of lead. The problem is to determine the percentage of neutrons which penetrate the wall. For simplicity we assume that the wall is of constant thickness 3d and neutrons enter the wall at right angles. A neutron travels a distance d before colliding with an atom of lead, and then rebounds in a random direction. The neutron then travels a further distance d before the next collision and so on. Finally we assume that at the tenth collision the neutron is absorbed. We wish to determine

(a) The fraction of neutrons which penetrate through the wall.

(b) The fraction of neutrons which are absorbed within the wall.

(c) The fraction of neutrons which return inside the reactor.

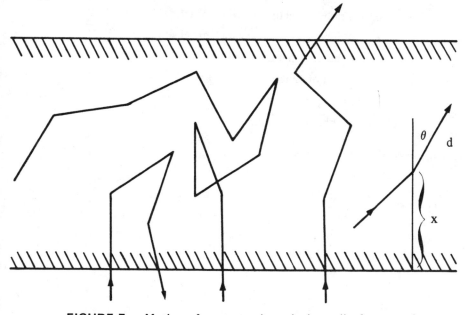

FIGURE 5a: Motion of neutrons through the wall of an atomic reactor.

*This example was developed from problem 30.2 of Scheid, F., *Schaum's Outline of Theory and Problems of Numerical Analysis,* McGraw-Hill, New York, 1968.

Figure 5a shows typical paths for three neutrons.

This problem cannot be solved analytically. However we can obtain estimates of the three quantities we are interested in by simulating the motion of the neutrons through the wall. Let us consider how we can simulate the motion of a single neutron. We assume the neutron has penetrated a distance x into the wall and is about to collide with an atom of lead. It rebounds in a direction θ which is a random number in the interval $(0, 2\pi)$, (see Figure 5a). To obtain this direction we select a random number z in the interval $(0, 1)$ and multiply by 2π. The depth of penetration x is then changed to

$$x \leftarrow x + d \cos \theta$$

Note that since θ lies in the interval $(0, 2\pi)$, $\cos \theta$ lies in the interval $(-1, 1)$. If the new value of x exceeds 3d then the neutron penetrates the wall. If x is less than zero the neutron returns inside the reactor. If x lies between 0 and 3d then we consider the next collision. We repeat the process until either the neutron leaves the wall or is absorbed at the tenth collision. Figure 5b contains a flowchart of a computer simulation of the motion of 5000 neutrons. The number of neutrons which penetrate np, which are absorbed na and which return nr are computed and printed at the end of the simulation.

np = number of neutrons which penetrate

na = number of neutrons which are absorbed

nr = number of neutrons which return

x = depth of penetration

n = number of collisions

count = number of neutrons

(Figure 5b continued on page 83.)

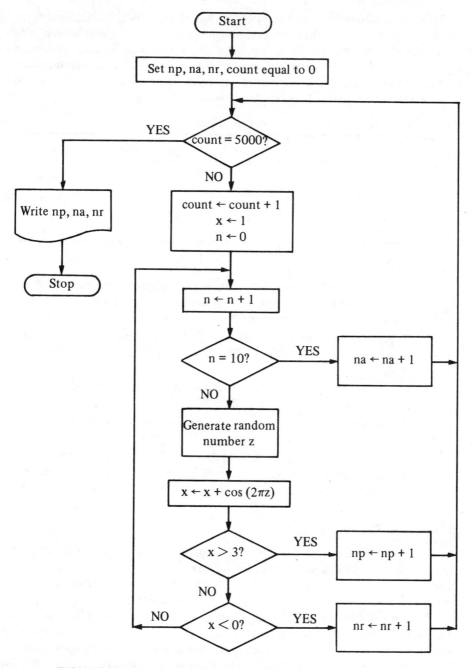

FIGURE 5b: Simulation of neutron diffusion.

Table 5c shows typical results for 100, 1000, 3000, and 5000 neutrons entering the wall. It appears that the percentage penetration is approximately 26%. This is clearly too large, and the designers of the reactor may wish the simulation repeated with the wall thickness increased. Even though this simulation might have to be repeated with several different thicknesses for the wall, this would certainly be more efficient than building several different reactors.

Table 5c: Results of neutron simulation.

Number of neutrons	% penetration	% absorbed	% returned
100	30.0	28.0	42.0
1000	26.0	23.4	50.6
3000	26.5	21.8	51.7
5000	26.3	22.0	51.7

Exercises

4. Write a computer program to simulate the neutron diffusion problem, and determine the fraction of neutrons which penetrate, are absorbed, and return. Use 5000 neutrons in your simulation.

5. Simulate the motion of 20 neutrons and record both the x and y coordinates at each collision. Plot a graph of the paths of these neutrons.

6. Repeat Exercise 4 with the thickness of the wall increased to 4d, and also with the thickness increased to 5d.

7. Suppose that at each collision, a neutron rebounds in a random direction which is restricted to lie within 90 degrees of its direction before collision. Simulate the motion of 5000 neutrons with this modification.

8. Repeat Exercise 4 but assume that a neutron enters the wall in a random direction instead of at right angles.

4. Airplane Traffic Flow

At an airport, airplanes land and take off on the same runway. Each airplane takes 3 minutes to land and 2 minutes to take off. On average 8 airplanes land and 8 take off in an hour. We shall assume that airplanes arrive at random instants of time. Although they are supposed to land and take off according to a schedule, in practice delays make the assumption of randomness quite reasonable. We are concerned with a queueing process where the service facility is the runway and there are two types of queue; a queue of airplanes in the air waiting to land, and a queue of airplanes on the ground waiting to take off. Since it is much more expensive to keep an airplane airborne than to have one waiting on the ground, we shall assume that an airplane wishing to land has priority over one wishing to take off. This is known as the queue discipline.

To make a probabilistic model of the operation of the airport we select a time interval of 1 minute. Landing (or take-off) arrivals occur at an average rate of 8 per hour. The probability that an arrival occurs in a one minute interval is thus 8/60, and that no arrival occurs is 52/60. To simulate landing arrivals, for each one minute interval we generate a random number. If it is less than 8/60 then a landing arrival occurs and this airplane joins the queue of airplanes wishing to land. We denote this queue by Q1. If an arrival occurs, we assume that it occurs at the end of the time interval. We generate another random number to determine if a take-off arrival occurs, and if so, it joins the take-off queue Q2. We next check to determine if the runway is free. If the runway is not free, we print the state of the system and consider the next time interval. If the runway is free, we first check the landing queue Q1, and if it is greater than zero we allow the first airplane in the landing queue to land. If Q1 equals zero, then we consider the queue Q2 of airplanes wishing to take off. A flowchart for the simulation of the airport for an 8 hour period is given in Figure 5c.

We may also include in our simulation a statistical summary to compute the average queue lengths and also the average time an airplane spends in a queue. We may also wish to observe how the system operates when we increase the arrival pattern from 8 airplanes (of each type) per hour to say 10 airplanes.

t = time in minutes

runway = time at which the runway is next available

$$test = \begin{cases} 0 & \text{if no airplane is on the runway} \\ 1 & \text{if a landing airplane is on the runway} \\ 2 & \text{if a take-off airplane is on the runway} \end{cases}$$

$Q1$ = number of airplanes waiting to land

$Q2$ = number of airplanes waiting to take off

dep = number of airplanes which have taken off at time t $\left\{\begin{array}{l}\text{These also include} \\ \text{airplanes on the} \\ \text{runway}\end{array}\right.$

arr = number of airplanes which have landed at time t

z = random number in the interval $(0,1)$

(Figure 5c continued on page 86.)

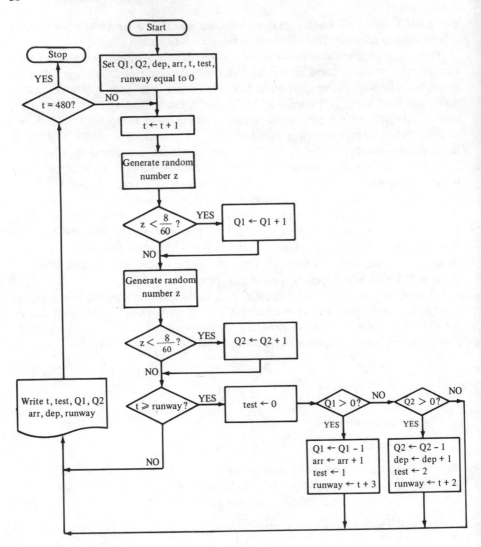

FIGURE 5c: Simulation of an airport.

Exercises

9. Write a computer program to simulate the operation of the airport. Your program should compute the average queue lengths and also the average waiting times (excluding runway times) for both landing and take-off airplanes.

10. Repeat the airport simulation, but assume that an airplane takes 4

minutes to land and 3 minutes to take off. How does this affect the average waiting times and queue lengths?

11. Repeat Exercise 9 with the arrival rate increased to 10 airplanes per hour.

5. Processing Computer Programs

A university has a computer on which student jobs are run. Students arrive at the computer at an average rate of 200 per hour, and queue if necessary. When they reach the front of the queue, they hand their job to the operator. Student jobs are of two types. Type 1 jobs fail to run, and these take 10 seconds. Type 2 jobs are jobs which run successfully, and these take 20 seconds. On average, half the student jobs fail, and half run successfully. We wish to determine the average queue length and the average turnaround time. This is a queueing process in which there is one queue and one service facility, but variable service time.

To simulate the operation of this process, we select a small time interval and assume that events occur only at the end of each interval. In this instance a 5 second time interval is appropriate. If we assume that students arrive at the computer at random instants of time, then since they arrive at an average rate of 200 per hour, the probability that a student arrives in a 5 second interval is $200/(60 \times 12) = 5/18$. For each time interval we generate a random number. If it is less than $5/18$ an arrival occurs. If it is greater than or equal to $5/18$ then no arrival occurs in that time interval. When a student job is read into the computer we wish to determine if it fails (10 second job) or runs successfully (20 second job). Since half the jobs fail, we generate a random number, and if it is less than $1/2$ the job fails, otherwise the job runs successfully. A flowchart for a computer simulation of the processing of jobs for a one hour period is given in Figure 5d. As in the airport simulation, this flowchart does not incorporate a statistical summary to compute the average queue length, average waiting time, average time the computer is not used, etc. In practice this statistical summary is an essential part of the simulation.

t = time in seconds

tf = time at which the computer is next free

Q = number of students in the queue

$$type = \begin{cases} 0 & \text{if no students} \\ 1 & \text{if 10-second failing job} \\ 2 & \text{if 20-second successful job} \end{cases}$$

arr = number of arrivals

z = random number

(Figure 5d continued on page 88.)

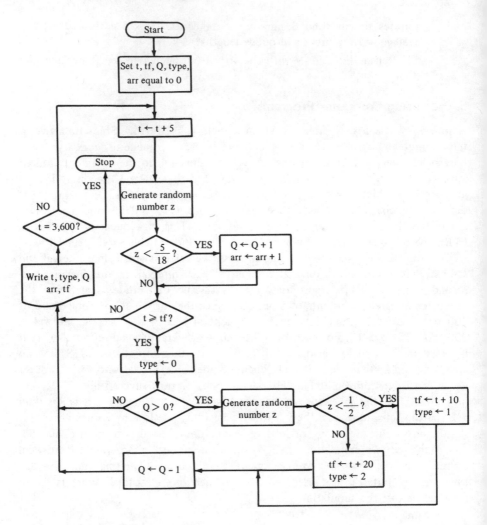

FIGURE 5d: Simulation of the processing of computer jobs.

Exercises

12. Write a computer program to simulate the processing of jobs on a computer. Compute the average queue length and the average waiting time excluding service. What fraction of the time is the computer free?

13. Repeat Exercise 12 with the arrival rate reduced to 150 students per hour. How does this affect the average queue length and average waiting time?

14. Suppose that the computer operator has some other jobs which take precisely one minute each, and that whenever the computer is free he runs one of these jobs. Simulate the operation of the computer assuming an arrival rate of 150 students per hour and determine how this affects the average queue length and average waiting time.

15. Repeat Exercise 12, but assume that a student job can take either 5, 10, 15, 20, or 25 seconds, each with probability 1/5. Determine the average queue length and waiting time excluding service.

6. Summary

The examples discussed in this chapter serve to demonstrate the basic techniques of simulation. However it must be realized that these examples are simplifications of the actual physical processes involved, and that a practical model of a physical process will in general be much more complicated. Many of the applications of simulation are concerned with queueing processes. There does exist a mathematical theory of queues which can sometimes be used to solve these problems analytically. However, for many practical problems, simulation is the only feasible technique available. One disadvantage of simulation techniques is that it is only possible to obtain approximate results by these methods. If we increase the length of the simulation by a factor of n, the expected accuracy improves by $\sqrt{n}$. Thus simulating a system for 100 hours tends to give 10 times the accuracy of a one hour simulation. However, with the advent of the electronic computer, and the appearance of special simulation programming languages, simulation has become a powerful method of obtaining approximate solutions to many difficult problems in science and engineering. It is usually much faster and more economical to observe the operation of a system under varying conditions using a simulation model, than to observe the operation of the system itself.

Exercises

16. Determine by simulation the average number of times a dice must be rolled so that all the numbers 1–6 inclusive occur at least once.

17. In the game of dice, a player throws two dice. If he throws 7 or 11 he wins immediately. If he throws 2, 3, or 12, he loses immediately. If he throws any other number, it is called the point, and he continues to throw until either the point appears again (in which case he wins) or until he throws 7 (in which case he loses). Simulate a player playing this game 1000 times and determine the fraction of times that he wins.

18. The organizers of a bridge tournament wish to have the cards 'dealt' by a computer. Write a computer program to do this. (Hint: Identify the cards of the deck with the integers 1, 2,...,52. To simulate the

shuffling of the deck of cards you require a random permutation of these integers. See Exercise 3 of Chapter 7.)

19. At a casino, the following game is played between a player and the banker. The player pays the banker $7.50. The banker has a roulette wheel with 36 numbers (1–36), which he spins. Assume the resulting number is 17. The banker then pays the player $1, and spins the wheel again. Suppose the number this time is 24. The banker pays another $1, and the process continues until a number is produced which has already occurred. Suppose the sequence of numbers is 17, 24, 18, 31. The banker has paid the player $4. At the next turn of the wheel, the number is 18 (a number already produced). At this point the game ends, and the player has lost $3.50. Simulate 200 such games, and print the numbers produced by the roulette wheel, the amount the player wins or loses each game, and the player's total loss or gain.

20. Simulate a player playing the game of snakes and ladders, and determine the average number of throws of the dice to complete the game.

21. A man runs a shooting gallery. He charges 25 cents for 3 shots at some clay plates which break when hit. If a person breaks 3 plates with his 3 shots he wins a prize which costs the man 1 dollar. Each broken plate costs the man 4 cents to replace. The probability that a person hits a plate on a single shot is 1/2. Write a program to simulate 1000 people playing the game and determine the average amount of money the man makes per player.

22. The weather in the land of Oz is either rain, fair or snow. Tomorrow's weather depends upon today's weather as indicated by the probabilities in the table.

| | | Tomorrow | | |
		rain	fair	snow
	rain	.5	.25	.25
Today	fair	.5	0	.5
	snow	.25	.25	.5

Thus, if it is raining today, for example, the probabilities of rain, fair, or snow tomorrow are .5, .25, .25 respectively. Simulate the weather for 1000 days, and determine the number of days with each type of weather. Start the simulation with fair weather.

23. A gas station has two gas pumps. Cars arrive at an average rate of 20 per hour. The service time for each car is either 3, 4, 5, 6 or 7

minutes, each with probability 1/5. Simulate the operation of the gas station for 8 hours assuming that a car arriving with both pumps occupied, drives on. Determine the fraction of customers lost. How is this affected if the gas station has 3 pumps?

24. At a telephone exchange there are 4 operators. Calls arrive at the exchange at random, at an average rate of 4 per minute. Each call occupies an operator for either 10, 20, 30, 40, 50, 60, or 70 seconds, each with probability 1/7. Simulate the handling of calls at the exchange for a 4 hour period, and determine the fraction of time an operator is free, the fraction of calls that are answered immediately, and the average time a subscriber has to wait before an operator answers his call. Use a 5 second time interval for the simulation.

25. A bank has 4 tellers. Customers arrive at an average rate of 4 per minute and select the shortest queue. The service times for a customer are given in the following table.

service time in seconds	20	30	40	50	60	70	80
probability	.1	.1	.2	.2	.2	.1	.1

Simulate the operation of the bank and determine the average queue length and the average waiting time (excluding service). Use a 5 second time interval for your simulation. How are these figures affected by using 5 tellers in place of 4?

26. A supermarket has 3 checkout counters. The time between successive customers arriving at the checkout counters is a random number between 0 and 30 seconds. A customer chooses the counter with the smallest queue. The service time at the counters is a random number between 0 and 75 seconds. Simulate the operation of the system for a 4 hour period and determine the average total service time (queue time and service time). Repeat the simulation with 4 checkout counters and compare the total service times. (Note that in this simulation, time is not increased by a fixed small amount, but is increased by a variable amount. This is an example of a continuous simulation as opposed to the discrete simulations discussed in this chapter.)

27. At an airport, passengers leaving an airplane have to pass through a passport control desk and a customs desk. The passengers form a single queue at the passport control desk where the service time for each passenger is a random number between 0 and 30 seconds. A passenger then goes immediately to the customs desk and queues again (if necessary). The service time at the customs desk is a random number between

0 and 25 seconds. Simulate this operation assuming that there are 200 passengers on the airplane, and determine the total time to handle all the passengers. Repeat the simulation assuming that there are two passport control desks and two customs desks, and that a passenger leaving a passport control desk selects the customs desk with the shorter queue. You may also assume that the passengers initially form a single queue of length 200, and move to whichever passport desk is next free.

Further Reading

Gordon, G., *System Simulation,* Prentice-Hall, New Jersey, 1969.

Hammersley, J. M. and D. C. Handscomb, *Monte Carlo Methods,* John Wiley, New York, 1964.

Sasieni, M., A. Yaspan, and L. Friedman, *Operations Research – Methods and Problems,* John Wiley, New York, 1959.

Tocher, K. D., *The Art of Simulation,* English Universities Press, London, 1963.

Wagner, H. M., *Principles of Operations Research With Applications to Managerial Decisions,* Prentice-Hall, New Jersey, 1969.

Linear Programming

1. Introduction

During the past twenty-five years, a powerful new mathematical technique called linear programming has been developed and applied successfully to a great variety of problems from science, industry, and commerce. A linear programming problem can be defined as any problem in which the objective is to maximize or minimize a linear function which is subject to linear constraints.

The simplex method, due to G. B. Dantzig, is a systematic procedure for solving a general linear programming problem. It is rather an involved and intricate technique to program for a computer. However, it is not possible to solve any but the smallest of linear programming problems without using this method. Nevertheless, if Dantzig's discovery had preceded the era of the high-speed computer, rather than coinciding with its birth, the simplex method would probably have been dismissed as being unwieldy. As it is, linear programming and its extensions must surely rate as one of the most useful discoveries in applied mathematics.

This chapter is quite ambitious in its scope. However, by concentrating on the simplest type of linear programming problem, and by discussing thoroughly a simple introductory problem we are led gradually to a description and flowchart of the simplex method. Finally, two quite distinct problems are considered which can both be solved by linear programming. Further applications of linear programming are included in the exercises at the end of the chapter.

2. A Simple Linear Programming Problem

We can illustrate the nature of linear programming problems by considering the following example.

Example 6–1. A small machine shop manufactures two items, Product A and Product B, by utilizing a grinder and a polisher according to the following schedule.

	Grinder	Polisher	Profit
Product A	4 hrs.	1 hr.	$4
Product B	3 hrs.	3 hrs.	$6

The shop works a 36-hour week, and it contains 4 grinders and 3 polishers. Assuming that they sell all they produce, how many of each item should be manufactured in order to maximize the profit?

The first step in solving this problem is to introduce a notation which allows the problem to be clearly stated in mathematical form. Accordingly, let A denote the weekly production of Product A, and let B be the weekly production of Product B. Then the weekly profit P is equal to $(4A + 6B)$. The total time available per week on the grinders is 144 hours, while 108 hours of polishing time are provided. Mathematically, the problem can now be stated as follows:

$$\text{Maximize} \quad 4A + 6B$$

$$\text{subject to} \quad 4A + 3B \leqslant 144 \tag{6.1}$$

$$A + 3B \leqslant 108 \tag{6.2}$$

$$A, B \geqslant 0. \tag{6.3}$$

The inequalities (6.1), (6.2), and (6.3) are referred to as the constraints for the problem. These constraints are displayed graphically in Figure 6a.

The inequalities (6.3) ensure that whatever quantities of Product A and Product B are decided upon, the shop will not be required to manufacture a negative amount of either! The inequalities (6.1) and (6.2) express, respectively, the restrictions imposed on any weekly manufacturing scheme by the total amount of grinding and polishing time available. These constraints must all be obeyed simultaneously, and together they define a feasible region as shown in Figure 6a. Only the points (A, B) in this feasible region can be considered when searching for the right combination that yields a maximum profit.

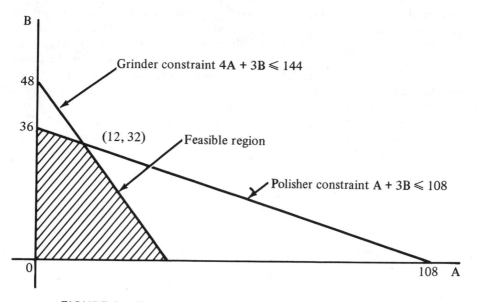

FIGURE 6a: The constraints combine to form a feasible region.

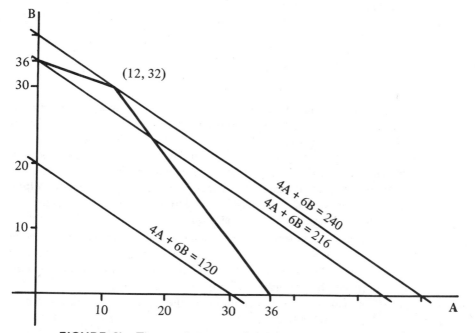

FIGURE 6b: The maximum profit occurs at a corner point of the feasible region.

Referring now to Figure 6b, we see that certain values of the profit P are attainable while others are not. In any event, having drawn the line 4A + 6B = P for some given profit P, say P = 120, the line corresponding to any other value of P is parallel to this first line. The solution to the problem can thus be found graphically by moving a line across the feasible region, keeping it parallel to the first line, until the value of P cannot be increased any further without leaving the feasible region. For this problem the maximum profit attainable is $240, and this profit is provided by manufacturing 12 of Product A and 32 of Product B. That is to say, the maximum of our linear programming problem occurs at a corner point, the point (12, 32), of the feasible region.

Exercises

1. Solve the following linear programming problems graphically

   a. Maximize $x + y$

       subject to $2x + y \leqslant 2$

$$x + 3y \leqslant 3$$
$$x, y \geqslant 0.$$

   b. Maximize $x + 2y$

       subject to $-x + 2y \leqslant 8$

$$x + y \leqslant 12$$
$$x + 3y \leqslant 18$$
$$x, y \geqslant 0.$$

2. A company produces two types of cars: a deluxe and a standard model. The respective profits are $120 and $90. The supply of parts is sufficient for only 1600 cars a day (deluxe and standard combined). The deluxe car has a larger engine of which only 800 per day are available. There are 1400 standard engines available per day. The deluxe car requires four coats of paint and the standard car requires two. There is sufficient time for a total of 4000 coats of paint per day. Formulate this as a linear programming problem and determine the optimal production plan graphically.

3. A company produces nails and screws. The company can make at most 4 million nails per day and at most 6 million screws per day. A screw requires 2 ounces of steel to produce and a nail requires 3 ounces. The company has available 18 million ounces of steel per day. The profit on nails is 3 cents per hundred and on screws 5 cents per hundred. How many nails and screws should the company manufacture each day to maximize its profits?

3. The General Linear Programming Problem

Given a linear programming problem which has a finite solution, then, motivated by the preceding example, we can make three observations which are always valid.

First, the diagram in Figure 6c shows that a procedure for maximization can also be used for minimization. More specifically,

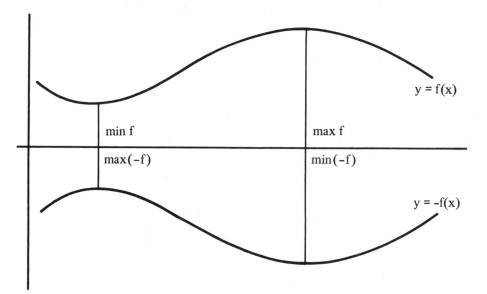

FIGURE 6c: The optimum values of f yield the optima of (−f).

$$\max f = -\min(-f) \text{ and } \min f = -\max(-f).$$

We shall state the general linear programming problem as a maximization problem; therefore this covers minimization too.

Secondly, the set of constraints to a linear programming problem, i.e. the feasible region, is a convex set. By this, we mean that any two points of the set can be joined by a straight line segment that lies in the set. Figure 6d contains some simple geometric examples of both convex and nonconvex sets.

Finally, the solution to a linear programming problem occurs at some corner point of the convex feasible region. Clearly, if the profit function of Example 6−1 was parallel to one side of the feasible region, the solution would occur at more than just a corner point (see Exercise 4-e). However, by concentrating our attention on the corner points we are able to locate a solution.

The simplex method, which we shall discuss in the next section, is a procedure for solving any linear programming problem. The method allows us to identify the corner points of the feasible region, and to narrow down our search of these extreme points until the maximum is located at one of them. However, before describing this procedure, we must first state the problem at hand in a general form.

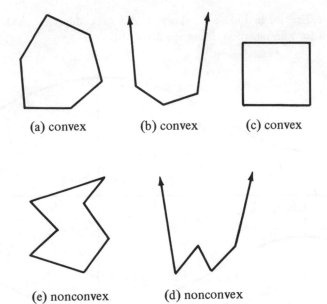

(a) convex   (b) convex   (c) convex

(e) nonconvex   (d) nonconvex

FIGURE 6d: A convex set contains the line segment joining any two of its points.

For our purposes, the general linear programming problem is defined as follows.

$$\text{Maximize} \quad c_1 x_1 + c_2 x_2 + \cdots + c_n x_n$$

$$\text{subject to} \quad a_{1,1} x_1 + a_{1,2} x_2 + \cdots + a_{1,n} x_n \leqslant b_1$$

$$a_{2,1} x_1 + a_{2,2} x_2 + \cdots + a_{2,n} x_n \leqslant b_2$$

$$\vdots$$

$$a_{m,1} x_1 + a_{m,2} x_2 + \cdots + a_{m,n} x_n \leqslant b_m$$

$$x_1, x_2, \cdots , x_n \qquad \geqslant 0$$

where $a_{1,1}, \ldots a_{m,n}$, $b_1, \ldots, b_m$, $c_1, \ldots, c_n$ are all known constants. Furthermore b_1, $b_2, \ldots, b_m \geqslant 0$.

The restriction that $b_i \geqslant 0$ for $i = 1, 2, \ldots, m$ is not normally insisted upon by most authors of linear programming texts. However, by concentrating our attention on this smaller class of problems for which this restriction is appropriate, the simplex method can be presented in its simplest form. The method can be extended to deal with negative values of b_i and also equality constraints, but we shall not discuss this.

4. The Simplex Method

The simplex method is composed of three stages, where the second and third stages are repeated over and over until a solution is found. The problem is first set up in a special table. Secondly, a particular number in the table, called the pivot, is chosen. Finally, the table is transformed by operating on all of its entries with the pivot.

We shall introduce the simplex method by applying it to the problem from Example 6–1. Thus, we wish to solve:

$$\text{Maximize} \quad 4x_1 + 6x_2 \tag{6.4}$$

$$\text{subject to} \quad 4x_1 + 3x_2 \leqslant 144 \tag{6.5}$$

$$x_1 + 3x_2 \leqslant 108 \tag{6.6}$$

$$x_1, x_2 \quad \geqslant 0 \tag{6.7}$$

The problem is first set up in a table.

4	3	144	③
1	$\boxed{3}$	108	④
−4	−6	0	
①	②		

The constraints (6.5) and (6.6) are entered in the first two rows, or rather the numbers from these constraints are recorded therein. The numbers from the expression (6.4), which is to be maximized, are then entered in the last row with their signs changed. A zero is inserted in the spare location in the last column of this third row. Finally, all of the columns except the last one, and all of the rows except the last one, are labelled in order as shown.

The pivot is chosen as some number from the upper-left portion of the table. The column from which the pivot is chosen is that column with the largest negative entry in the last row. In this case, the column labelled ② has an entry of −6 in the last row, and hence the pivot is chosen from this column. For each positive entry in the pivotal column, the ratio of the element in the last column to the element in this column is determined. The pivot is chosen as the entry in the pivotal column corresponding to the smallest ratio. Thus for our problem it is necessary to determine the smaller of 144/3 and 108/3. We have identified the pivot by enclosing it in a box.

The table is now transformed using the following set of rules. In the new table, the entries corresponding to the old pivotal row are obtained by dividing this row by the pivot. The entries corresponding to the old pivotal column are obtained by dividing this column by the pivot, and then changing the sign of all of these numbers. The pivot location itself is assigned the value of the reciprocal of the pivot. All other locations, including the entries in the bottom row and final column, are assigned the values obtained from the following "corner-point rule."

$$
\begin{array}{ccccccc}
\cdot & \cdot & \cdot & \cdot & \cdot & \cdot & \cdot \\
\cdot & a & \cdot & \cdot & \cdot & b & \cdot \\
\cdot & \cdot & \cdot & \cdot & \cdot & \cdot & \cdot \\
\cdot & c & \cdot & \cdot & \cdot & p & \cdot \\
\cdot & \cdot & \cdot & \cdot & \cdot & \cdot & \cdot
\end{array}
$$

Let a, b, c, and p be values from the original table, where p is the pivot, and b and c are the entries in the pivotal column and row, that lie horizontally and vertically opposite a. Then the new value for a is

$$a \leftarrow a - b \times c/p$$

Finally, the transformation of the table is completed by interchanging the two labels which are horizontally and vertically opposite the pivot. Using these transformation rules, the table then appears as follows.

$\boxed{3}$	-1	36	③
$1/3$	$1/3$	36	②
-2	2	216	
①	④		

We now return to the problem of choosing a pivot. Column 1 has the only negative entry in the bottom row, and the minimum positive ratio of 36/3 and $36/(1/3)$ occurs for the row labelled ③ . The pivot is thus determined. Applying the transformation rules to this table yields the final table.

$1/3$	$-1/3$	12	①
$-1/9$	$4/9$	32	②
$2/3$	$4/3$	240	
③	④		

In general, tables are transformed repeatedly in the simplex method until the stage is reached where no negative entries occur in the bottom row. When this occurs, the problem has been solved. The solution is found by inspecting the final column and noting the row labels corresponding to these entries. For our problem, the label ① tells us that $x_1 = 12$, the label ② means that $x_2 = 32$, and the resulting maximum value is 240. We note that this agrees with the graphical solution obtained previously. Although the final solution to this problem is integer valued, in general the solution to a linear programming problem will not have this property.

Example 6–2. As a second example we consider the following problem.

$$\text{Maximize} \quad -x_1 + 6x_2$$

$$\text{subject to} \quad 3x_1 - 2x_2 \leqslant 14$$

$$-2x_1 + 8x_2 \leqslant 24$$

$$-4x_1 + 6x_2 \leqslant 20$$

$$x_1, x_2 \geqslant 0.$$

The tables of the simplex method are given below.

3	−2	14	③
−2	$\boxed{8}$	24	④
−4	6	20	⑤
1	−6	0	
①	②		

$\boxed{\dfrac{5}{2}}$	$\dfrac{1}{4}$	20	③
$-\dfrac{1}{4}$	$\dfrac{1}{8}$	3	②
$-\dfrac{5}{2}$	$-\dfrac{3}{4}$	2	⑤
$-\dfrac{1}{2}$	$\dfrac{3}{4}$	18	
①	④		

$$\begin{array}{cc|cc}
\dfrac{2}{5} & \dfrac{1}{10} & 8 & \textcircled{1} \\[2ex]
\dfrac{1}{10} & \dfrac{3}{20} & 5 & \textcircled{2} \\[2ex]
1 & -\dfrac{1}{2} & 22 & \textcircled{5} \\[2ex]
\hline
\dfrac{1}{5} & \dfrac{4}{5} & 22 & \\[2ex]
\textcircled{3} & \textcircled{4} & &
\end{array}$$

After two iterations we see that no negative entries occur in the bottom row and hence this table contains the final solution given by $x_1 = 8$, $x_2 = 5$, and the resulting maximum value is 22. Note that the label $\textcircled{5}$ appears in the right hand column of the final table. This label, being originally assigned to a row, is ignored.

In the final table of any given problem, the column of labels on the right side of the table will be some combination of the labels $\textcircled{1}$, $\textcircled{2}$,..., $\textcircled{n}$, $\textcircled{n+1}$,..., $\textcircled{n+m}$. Generally these are not in any particular order, and only those labels from $\textcircled{1}$ up to $\textcircled{n}$ have any meaning as variables. Thus the values corresponding to the labels from $\textcircled{n+1}$ to $\textcircled{n+m}$ are ignored.

We shall now state the rules for the three stages of the simplex method as it is implemented on a computer. Notice that, due to the fact that real numbers are not represented exactly on a computer, we define a small positive number ϵ, and say that a quantity is positive only if it exceeds ϵ, and is negative only if it is less than $-\epsilon$. Referring to the general linear programming problem stated earlier, the rules for simplex method are as follows.

Stage A   (a)   Read m, n, ϵ

(b)   Read a_{ij} for $i = 1, 2,...,m; j = 1, 2,...,n$

(c)   Read b_i for $i = 1, 2,...,m$ and put $a_{i,n+1} = b_i$

(d)   Read c_j for $j = 1, 2,...,n$ and put $a_{m+1,j} = -c_j$

(e)   Define $a_{m+1,n+1} = 0$

(f)   Assign labels to rows and columns, by defining $a_{m+2,j} = j$ for $j = 1, 2,...,n$ and $a_{i,n+2} = n + i$ for $i = 1, 2,...,m$

Stage B   (a)   Calculate $\min(a_{m+1,j})$ for $j = 1, 2,...,n$. Suppose $\min(a_{m+1,j}) = a_{m+1,in}$, i.e. the minimum occurs when $j = in$. Finish calculation if $a_{m+1,in} > -\epsilon$.

(b) Calculate $\min(a_{i,n+1}/a_{i,\text{in}})$ for $i = 1, 2,...,m$ and $a_{i,\text{in}} > \epsilon$. Suppose this minimum occurs when $i = \text{out}$. Then the pivot is $a_{\text{out},\text{in}}$.

Stage C

(a) $a_{i,j} \leftarrow a_{i,j} - \left\{\dfrac{a_{i,\text{in}}}{a_{\text{out},\text{in}}}\right\} \times a_{\text{out},j}$ for $i = 1, 2,...,m + 1$; and $i \neq \text{out}$
$j = 1, 2,...,n + 1$
$j \neq \text{in}$

(b) $a_{\text{out},j} \leftarrow a_{\text{out},j}/a_{\text{out},\text{in}}$ for $j = 1, 2,...,n + 1$; $j \neq \text{in}$

(c) $a_{i,\text{in}} \leftarrow -a_{i,\text{in}}/a_{\text{out},\text{in}}$ for $i = 1, 2,...,m + 1$; $i \neq \text{out}$

(d) $a_{\text{out},\text{in}} \leftarrow 1/a_{\text{out},\text{in}}$

(e) Interchange labels opposite the pivot.

(f) Repeat stages B and C until the solution is obtained.

Note that we have stored b_1, b_2,...,b_m and c_1, c_2,...,c_n in the subscripted variable a. Combining this list of instructions with the flowchart below, the programming of the simplex method reduces to an almost routine exercise for the reader.

Exercises

4. Solve the following linear programming problems graphically.

a. Maximize $\quad 4x_1 + x_2$

subject to $\quad x_1 + x_2 \leqslant 7$

$\qquad\qquad 2x_1 - x_2 \leqslant 3$

$\qquad\qquad 2x_1 + 4x_2 \leqslant 24$

$\qquad\qquad 4x_1 - x_2 \leqslant 8$

$\qquad\qquad x_1, x_2 \geqslant 0$

b. Maximize $\quad 2x_1 + 5x_2$

subject to $\quad x_1 \qquad\quad \leqslant 400$

$\qquad\qquad\qquad x_2 \leqslant 300$

$\qquad\qquad x_1 + x_2 \leqslant 500$

$\qquad\qquad x_1, x_2 \geqslant 0$

c. Maximize $\quad 2x_1 + x_2$

subject to $\quad x_1 + x_2 \leqslant 6$

$\qquad\qquad x_1 - x_2 \leqslant 3$

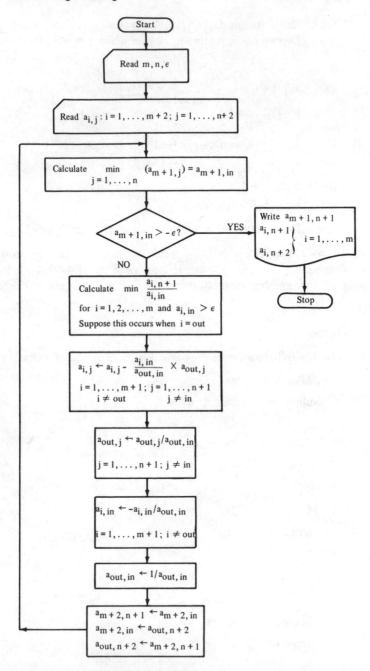

FIGURE 6e: The simplex method for linear programming.

$$5x_1 + 2x_2 \leqslant 20$$
$$x_1, x_2 \quad \geqslant 0$$

d. Maximize x_1

subject to $x_1 + 2x_2 \leqslant 2$

$$2x_1 + x_2 \leqslant 2$$
$$2x_1 - 4x_2 \leqslant 1$$
$$x_1, x_2 \quad \geqslant 0$$

e. Maximize $x_1 + x_2$

subject to $x_1 \qquad \leqslant 4$

$$x_2 \leqslant 5$$
$$x_1 + x_2 \leqslant 6$$
$$x_1, x_2 \quad \geqslant 0.$$

Is the solution unique?

f. Maximize $x_1 + x_2$

subject to $x_1 - x_2 \leqslant 1$

$$-2x_1 + x_2 \leqslant 2$$
$$x_1, x_2 \quad \geqslant 0$$

Does an optimum solution exist?

5. Write a computer program to solve a linear programming problem by the simplex method. Use this program to solve the first five problems of Exercise 4.

6. Solve the following linear programming problems.

a. Maximize $3x_1 + 2x_2 + 8x_3$

subject to $6x_1 + 6x_2 + 10x_3 \leqslant 25$

$$3x_1 + 8x_2 + 10x_3 \leqslant 20$$
$$x_1, x_2, x_3 \qquad \geqslant 0$$

b. Maximize $3x_1 + 4x_2 + 5x_3$

subject to $2x_1 \qquad + 3x_3 \leqslant 16$

$$5x_2 + 2x_3 \leqslant 20$$
$$3x_1 + 4x_2 + 2x_3 \leqslant 30$$
$$x_1, x_2, x_3 \qquad \geqslant 0$$

c. Maximize $x_1 + x_2 + x_3$
    subject to $-2x_1 - 2x_2 \qquad \leqslant 10$
                 $x_1 + 4x_2 - 3x_3 \leqslant 6$
                 $6x_1 + 4x_2 + 5x_3 \leqslant 10$
                 $x_1, x_2, x_3 \qquad \geqslant 0$

d. Maximize $3x_1 + 2x_2 + 4x_3$
    subject to $x_1 + x_2 + x_3 \leqslant 12$
                 $x_1 - x_2 - 2x_3 \leqslant 5$
                 $x_1 + x_2 - x_3 \leqslant 2$
                 $x_1, x_2, x_3 \qquad \geqslant 0$

e. Maximize $4x_1 + 7x_2 + 5x_3 - x_4$
    subject to $x_1 + x_2 + x_3 - x_4 \leqslant 5$
                 $x_1 - 2x_2 + 2x_3 + 4x_4 \leqslant 12$
                 $2x_1 + 3x_2 - x_3 + 4x_4 \leqslant 10$
                 $x_1, x_2, x_3, x_4 \qquad \geqslant 0$

f. Maximize $8x_1 + x_2 + 3x_3 + 7x_4 + 2x_5 + 7x_6 + x_7$
    subject to $6x_1 + 5x_2 + 5x_3 + 7x_4 + 9x_5 \qquad\qquad \leqslant 3$
                 $4x_1 + 3x_2 + 5x_3 + 6x_4 + 8x_5 + 5x_6 + 8x_7 \leqslant 5$
                 $9x_1 + 4x_2 + 8x_3 \qquad + 4x_5 + 8x_6 + 6x_7 \leqslant 3$
                 $5x_1 + 9x_2 + 2x_3 + 5x_4 + 7x_5 + 9x_6 + 3x_7 \leqslant 9$
                 $8x_1 + 5x_2 + 8x_3 + 9x_4 + 2x_5 + 5x_6 + 7x_7 \leqslant 6$
                 $x_1, x_2, x_3, x_4, x_5, x_6, x_7 \qquad\qquad \geqslant 0$

5. Theory of the Simplex Method

The rules of the simplex method have so far been presented without any explanation as to how the method works. In this section we include an elementary discussion of the theory of the simplex method.

We consider the simple activity analysis problem given in Example 6–1, namely

$$\text{Maximize} \quad z = 4x_1 + 6x_2 \tag{6.4}$$

$$\text{subject to} \quad 4x_1 + 3x_2 \leqslant 144 \tag{6.5}$$

$$x_1 + 3x_2 \leqslant 108 \tag{6.6}$$

$$x_1, x_2 \geqslant 0 \tag{6.7}$$

The function $z = 4x_1 + 6x_2$ which is to be maximized is referred to as the objective function.

We first define new nonnegative variables x_3, x_4 to be the difference between the right hand side and the left hand side of the constraints (6.5) and (6.6) respectively. Since these variables take up the slack in the inequalities, they are referred to as slack variables. The inequality constraints (6.5) and (6.6) are transformed into equality constraints and the problem becomes

$$\text{Maximize} \qquad z = 4x_1 + 6x_2 + 0x_3 + 0x_4 \qquad\qquad (6.8)$$

$$\text{subject to} \qquad 4x_1 + 3x_2 + x_3 \qquad\quad = 144 \qquad\qquad (6.9)$$

$$x_1 + 3x_2 \qquad + x_4 = 108 \qquad\qquad (6.10)$$

$$x_1, x_2, x_3, x_4 \qquad \geqslant 0 \qquad\qquad (6.11)$$

Thus we have two equations in the four unknowns x_1, x_2, x_3, x_4 which in general will have infinitely many solutions. We wish to determine the particular nonnegative solution which maximizes the objective function (6.8). The problem can be rewritten in the following form

$$4x_1 + 3x_2 + x_3 \qquad\quad = 144 \qquad\qquad (6.12)$$

$$x_1 + 3x_2 \qquad + x_4 = 108 \qquad\qquad (6.13)$$

$$z - 4x_1 - 6x_2 \qquad\qquad = 0 \qquad\qquad (6.14)$$

$$x_1, x_2, x_3, x_4 \qquad \geqslant 0 \qquad\qquad (6.15)$$

and we wish to determine the solution to these equations which maximizes z.

Referring to (6.12) and (6.13) we see that if we set $x_1 = 0$, $x_2 = 0$, we obtain a solution $x_3 = 144$, $x_4 = 108$, $z = 0$. This solution is represented by the following simplex table

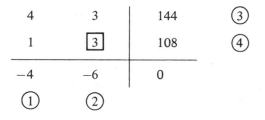

The objective function $z = 4x_1 + 6x_2$ can be increased by increasing either x_1 or x_2 from their present value of zero. Since the coefficient of x_2 is larger than that of x_1, the simplex algorithm selects x_2 as the variable to be increased. This corresponds to finding the most negative entry in the third row of the simplex table.

If we fix $x_1 = 0$ and increase x_2 while varying only x_3 and x_4, we see from equations (6.12) and (6.13) that we cannot increase x_2 indefinitely without forcing either x_3 or x_4 to become negative, and thus violating the nonnegativity constraint (6.15). The largest value of x_2 is thus min $\{144/3, 108/3\} = 108/3 = 36$ (see equations (6.12) and (6.13)). This makes the variable $x_4 = 0$. The element of the simplex table at which the minimum occurs is called the pivot and has been identified by enclosing it in a box. The new solution is given by $x_1 = 0$, $x_2 = 36$, $x_3 = 36$, $x_4 = 0$. The new value of the objective function is given by $z = 4x_1 + 6x_2 = 216$.

In order to determine if the objective function can be increased further, it is necessary to transform equations (6.12), (6.13) and (6.14). Equation (6.13) is normalized by dividing by the pivot element (in this case 3) to obtain equation (6.17). Equations (6.12) and (6.14) are now transformed by Gaussian elimination (see Chapter 3). This involves subtracting suitable multiples of equation (6.13) from equations (6.12) and (6.14) to eliminate x_2 from these equations. This produces the system

$$3x_1 \qquad + x_3 - \quad x_4 = 36 \qquad\qquad (6.16)$$

$$\frac{1}{3}x_1 + x_2 \qquad + \frac{1}{3}x_4 = 36 \qquad\qquad (6.17)$$

$$z - 2x_1 \qquad\qquad + 2x_4 = 216 \qquad\qquad (6.18)$$

These equations readily yield a solution $x_1 = 0$, $x_2 = 36$, $x_3 = 36$, $x_4 = 0$ with the value of the objective function $z = 216$. This solution is represented in the second simplex table.

$\boxed{3}$	-1	36	③
$1/3$	$1/3$	36	②
-2	2	216	
①	④		

We now proceed with the next iteration of the simplex method. The objective function $z = 216 + 2x_1 - 2x_4$ can be further increased if x_1 is increased from its present value of zero. Referring to equations (6.16) and (6.17), we wish to increase x_1 while keeping $x_4 = 0$ and only varying x_2 and x_3. The largest value that x_1 can have without making x_2 or x_3 negative is given by $x_1 = $ min $\{36/3, 36/(1/3)\} = 36/3 = 12$. Thus in the new solution x_3 is zero. Transforming the equations again we obtain

$$x_1 \quad + \frac{1}{3}x_3 - \frac{1}{3}x_4 = 12 \tag{6.19}$$

$$x_2 - \frac{1}{9}x_3 + \frac{4}{9}x_4 = 32 \tag{6.20}$$

$$z \quad + \frac{2}{3}x_3 + \frac{4}{3}x_4 = 240 \tag{6.21}$$

Here we have normalized equation (6.16) and eliminated x_1 from equations (6.17) and (6.18). The new solution given by $x_1 = 12$, $x_2 = 32$, $x_3 = 0$, $x_4 = 0$, $z = 240$ is represented in the third simplex table

1/3	−1/3	12	①
−1/9	4/9	32	②
2/3	4/3	240	
③	④		

From (6.21) we see that the objective function $z = 240 - 2/3\ x_3 - 4/3\ x_4$ cannot be increased further by making x_3 or x_4 positive. The solution represented in the third table of the simplex method is the final solution to the linear programming problem.

6. Two Applications of Linear Programming

The simplex method of linear programming has been used successfully to solve problems from a multitude of different sources. Linear programming has been applied to the oil industry, economics, diet problems, military operations, the construction industry, game theory, competitive bidding, network analysis, traffic analysis, and many other areas of human activity. Here we shall consider just two of the hundreds of applications of this powerful tool in detail, and discuss several other applications in the exercises at the end of the chapter.

Example 6–3. In this first application we shall consider the general activity-analysis problem; the simple problem in Example 6–1 is of this type.

A manufacturer has given amounts of different resources available. These may be raw materials, equipment, manpower, finances, etc. These are combined to produce several commodities. The manufacturer knows how much of resource i it takes to produce one unit of commodity j, and the profit involved. He wants to know which combination of commodities will maximize his total profit.

Let m = number of resources,

n = number of commodities,

$a_{i,j}$ = number of units of resource i required to produce one unit of commodity j,

b_i = maximum number of units of resource i available,

c_j = profit per unit of commodity j produced,

x_j = amount produced of commodity j.

With this notation the problem can be stated in linear programming form as follows.

$$\text{Maximize} \quad c_1x_1 + c_2x_2 + \cdots + c_nx_n$$
$$\text{subject to} \quad a_{1,1}x_1 + a_{1,2}x_2 + \cdots + a_{1,n}x_n \leq b_1$$
$$a_{2,1}x_1 + a_{2,2}x_2 + \cdots + a_{2,n}x_n \leq b_2$$
$$\vdots$$
$$a_{m,1}x_1 + a_{m,2}x_2 + \cdots + a_{m,n}x_n \leq b_m$$
$$x_1, x_2, \cdots, x_n \geq 0.$$

Exercises 7, 8, 9, 10 are specific examples that fall into this category.

Example 6–4. Find the straight line $y = a + bx$ which best fits the four points $\{(x_1,y_1), (x_2,y_2), (x_3,y_3), (x_4,y_4)\}$, in the minimax sense, i.e., so that the largest vertical displacement of the line from each point is as small as possible.

The diagram in Figure 6f shows how a line is positioned in order to achieve a "closest fit" in this sense.

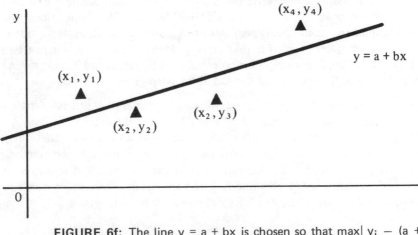

FIGURE 6f: The line $y = a + bx$ is chosen so that $\max_i | y_i - (a + bx_i)|$ is made as small as possible.

This problem can be recast as one in linear programming. For simplicity, we shall assume that $a \geqslant 0$, $b \geqslant 0$. Now for any fixed values of a and b, define $d = \max|y_i - (a + bx_i)|$, where clearly $d \geqslant 0$.

Then we wish to

$$\text{Minimize} \quad d$$
$$\text{subject to} \quad |y_1 - (a + bx_1)| \leqslant d$$
$$|y_2 - (a + bx_2)| \leqslant d$$
$$|y_3 - (a + bx_3)| \leqslant d$$
$$|y_4 - (a + bx_4)| \leqslant d$$

In order to remove the absolute value signs from the problem, we make use of the fact that $|z| \leqslant e$ is equivalent to stating that $z \leqslant e$ and $-z \leqslant e$ simultaneously. Thus, the problem becomes

$$\text{Minimize} \quad d$$
$$\text{subject to} \quad y_1 - (a + bx_1) \leqslant d$$
$$-y_1 + (a + bx_1) \leqslant d$$
$$\vdots \qquad\qquad \vdots$$
$$y_4 - (a + bx_4) \leqslant d$$
$$-y_4 + (a + bx_4) \leqslant d$$

Finally, dividing each inequality constraint by d, and defining $D = 1/d$, $A = a/d$, $B = b/d$, the following linear programming problem results. (Note that minimizing d is equivalent to maximizing D).

$$\text{Maximize} \quad D$$
$$\text{subject to} \quad y_1 D - A - x_1 B \leqslant 1$$
$$-y_1 D + A + x_1 B \leqslant 1$$
$$\vdots \qquad\qquad \vdots$$
$$y_4 D - A - x_4 B \leqslant 1$$
$$-y_4 D + A + x_4 B \leqslant 1$$
$$D, A, B \qquad \geqslant 0$$

Further applications of linear programming are given in the exercises at the end of the chapter.

Exercises

7. A furniture manufacturer makes three types of bookcases: A, B, and C. These products use two kinds of lumber, and he has available 1500 feet of the first kind and 1100 feet of the second. He has 800 man-hours available for the whole job. He cannot produce more than 100, 150, 200 bookcases of types A, B, C, respectively. Each bookcase of type A, B, C requires 5, 2, 8 feet of the first kind of lumber and 2, 3, 4 feet of the second kind of lumber respectively. Bookcase A requires 4 man-hours to make, bookcase B requires 3 man-hours and bookcase C requires 5 man-hours. The profit on each bookcase is $10, $5, $7 respectively. How many bookcases of each type should he make to maximize his profit?

8. A manufacturer can use one or more of four production processes. There are three inputs for each process: labour in man-hours, tons of raw material A, tons of raw material B. The manufacturer must determine the optimal production schedule given the following information:

	Process 1	Process 2	Process 3	Process 4	Input Available
Man-hours	4	2	4	2	400
Tons of A	4	6	10	12	2000
Tons of B	4	18	8	6	1500
Profit/unit	12	8	14	10	

Formulate this as a linear programming problem and determine the optimal production schedule.

9. A baker starts his day with a certain amount of flour, eggs and milk. He can make bread, cakes, muffins and cookies. How many should he make of each to maximize his profit?

	Flour (ounces)	Eggs	Milk (pints)	Profit (cents)
Bread	12	0	1/2	3/2
Cakes	3	3	1/4	1/2
Muffins	4	1	1/4	1
Cookies	2	1	0	1/2
Available	10,000	2,000	500	

10. A manufacturer produces two types of bearings, A and B, utilizing three types of machines: lathes, grinders, and drill presses. The machinery requirements for one unit of each product, in hours are expressed in the following table.

	Lathe	Grinder	Drill Press	Profit in cents
Bearing A	.02	.06	.06	10
Bearing B	.04	.02	.03	15
Weekly machine capacity	400	450	480	

a. Find the optimum production plan.

b. The manufacturer has enough money to buy one more machine of any kind, and by so doing he will increase the capacity of that type of machine by 40 hours per week. Which machine should he buy?

11. Determine the straight lines of the form $y = a + bx$ which best fit the following data in the minimax sense.

a.

x	0	2	3	5
y	2	4	6.5	12

b.

x	0	1	2	3	4	5
y	6.2	6.8	7.0	7.8	8.5	9.4

c.

x	10	20	30	40	50	60
y	11	17	22	24	32	37

d.

x	1.3	2.4	3.7	4.9	5.6	6.3
y	2.7	2.8	3.4	3.5	3.8	4.4

7. Summary

Since the discovery of the simplex method in 1947 for solving linear programs, the method has been applied to a great variety of problems in science, industry, commerce and military operations. Without the aid of a high speed computer most of these problems could not be solved. There are many extensions of linear programming which we have not discussed here. These include a modified version of the simplex method called the revised simplex method. This version is usually available as a standard software package in most computer centers concerned with scientific computation. Integer linear programming is concerned with linear programming problems where the variables are restricted to have integer values. More recently, techniques have been developed for nonlinear programming in which the variables may appear in a nonlinear form. However, a discussion of these more advanced topics is beyond the scope of this book. Applications of linear programming to game theory and network analysis are outlined in Exercises 12–16.

Exercises

12. Two players A and B play the following game. Player A first pays player B \$7. Each player then selects an integer 1, 2, or 3, and both declare simultaneously their selected number. Player B then pays player A an amount determined by the following table

Player B

		1	2	3
	1	6	8	2
Player A	2	4	6	12
	3	10	0	6

Thus if player A chooses 3 and player B chooses 1, player B pays \$10 to player A, and has clearly made a net loss of \$3. Player B decides to select his numbers at random with probabilities p_1, p_2, p_3. If player A always selects 1, in a large number of plays, player B expects to pay \$$(6p_1 + 8p_2 + 2p_3)$ per game. If player A always selects 2, then player B expects to pay \$$(4p_1 + 6p_2 + 12p_3)$, and if player A selects 3, player B expects to pay \$$(10p_1 + 6p_3)$. Player B wishes to minimize the amount he expects to pay to player A each game, whatever strategy player A adopts. He therefore decides to choose the probabilities p_1, p_2, p_3 which minimize the maximum possible amount he expects to pay player A. Denoting this by v, player B wishes to solve the following problem:

$$\text{Minimize} \quad v$$
$$\text{subject to} \quad 6p_1 + 8p_2 + 2p_3 \leqslant v$$
$$4p_1 + 6p_2 + 12p_3 \leqslant v$$
$$10p_1 \quad\quad + 6p_3 \leqslant v$$
$$p_1 + p_2 + p_3 = 1$$
$$p_1, p_2, p_3, v \geqslant 0.$$

The last constraint merely states that the sum of the probabilities equals one. If the minimum value of v is less than 7 (the amount player A pays each game), then player B expects to make a profit over a large number of plays of the game.

We may reformulate this problem by putting $x_i = p_i/v$, $i = 1, 2, 3$, and noting that $x_1 + x_2 + x_3 = (p_1 + p_2 + p_3)/v = 1/v$. Thus the minimization of v can be accomplished by maximizing $1/v$ or $x_1 + x_2 + x_3$, and we obtain the linear programming problem

$$\text{Maximize} \quad x_1 + x_2 + x_3$$
$$\text{subject to} \quad 6x_1 + 8x_2 + 2x_3 \leqslant 1$$
$$4x_1 + 6x_2 + 12x_3 \leqslant 1$$
$$10x_1 \qquad + 6x_3 \leqslant 1$$
$$x_1, x_2, x_3 \qquad \geqslant 0.$$

Having solved this problem, the maximum amount v that player B expects to pay player A is the reciprocal of the maximum value ($x_1 + x_2 + x_3$), and the probabilities are given by $p_i = v \, x_i$, $i = 1, 2, 3$. Determine player B's strategy and the maximum amount he expects to pay player A. Would you play this game? What strategy should player A adopt?

13. Determine the strategies for both players in the following games.

a)

5	2	4	5
3	7	6	4
2	8	1	1

b)

5	10	3
2	5	9
11	1	5

c)

7	5	3	10	8
6	8	5	4	7
4	8	6	6	3
3	4	7	5	5

In each case determine the amount player A should pay player B to make the game fair.

14. Two players are provided with an ace of diamonds and an ace of clubs. Player A is also given the two of diamonds and player B the two of clubs. Both players simultaneously show one of their cards. Player A wins if the suits match and player B wins if they do not. The amount of the pay-off is the numerical value of the card shown by the winner. If two deuces are shown, the pay-off is zero. Formulate this as a game and determine the best strategy for each player. Since the game will contain negative numbers (corresponding to player B winning), you must add a constant to all entries to make them nonnegative. This constant is then equivalent to the amount player A pays player B each game.

15. The operation of a water company can be represented by the following network.

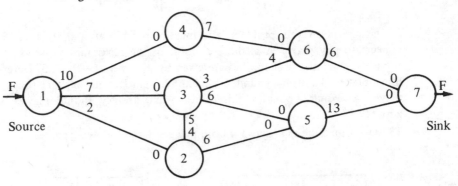

The circled numbers represent pumping stations, and the branches connecting them represent pipe lines. The numbers on a branch represent the maximum permissible flow along that branch. Thus along branch 1 → 4 there is a flow capacity of 10, and along branch 4 → 1 there can be no flow. Note that there can be a flow in both directions between stations 2 and 3. The problem is to determine the maximum possible flow from the source (1) to the sink (7). We may formulate this as a linear programming problem. We use variables $x_1, x_2, ..., x_{12}$ to denote the flows in the branches as follows.

Variable	Branch	Capacity
x_1	$1 \to 2$	2
x_2	$1 \to 3$	7
x_3	$1 \to 4$	10

x_4	$2 \rightarrow 3$	4
x_5	$2 \rightarrow 5$	6
x_6	$3 \rightarrow 2$	5
x_7	$3 \rightarrow 5$	6
x_8	$3 \rightarrow 6$	3
x_9	$4 \rightarrow 6$	7
x_{10}	$5 \rightarrow 7$	13
x_{11}	$6 \rightarrow 3$	4
x_{12}	$6 \rightarrow 7$	6

We see that the variables x_i must be nonnegative and must also satisfy the capacity limitations, $x_1 \leqslant 2$, $x_2 \leqslant 7,...,x_{12} \leqslant 6$. Also the flow into a station must equal the flow out of the station, and hence we have five conservation of flow constraints.

Station	Conservation of flow constraint
2	$x_1 + x_6 = x_4 + x_5$
3	$x_2 + x_4 + x_{11} = x_6 + x_7 + x_8$
4	$x_3 = x_9$
5	$x_5 + x_7 = x_{10}$
6	$x_8 + x_9 = x_{11} + x_{12}$

We wish to maximize the flow from source to sink. Thus we wish to maximize $F = x_1 + x_2 + x_3$. This is the flow from station 1, and by the conservation of flow constraints we can show that this is equal to the flow into station 7 $(x_{10} + x_{12})$. To handle the equality constraints we consider the conservation of flow constraint for station 2, namely,

$$x_1 - x_4 - x_5 + x_6 = 0.$$

We note that a constraint $z = 0$ is equivalent to two constraints $z \leqslant 0$, $z \geqslant 0$, or $z \leqslant 0$, $-z \leqslant 0$. Thus we may rewrite the constraint for station 2 as

$$x_1 - x_4 - x_5 + x_6 \leqslant 0$$
$$-x_1 + x_4 + x_5 - x_6 \leqslant 0.$$

We may formulate the problem in the following linear programming form.

Maximize $x_1 + x_2 + x_3$

subject to

$$
\begin{array}{llll}
x_1 & -x_4 - x_5 + x_6 & & \leq 0 \\
-x_1 & +x_4 + x_5 - x_6 & & \leq 0 \\
x_2 & +x_4 \quad -x_6 - x_7 - x_8 & +x_{11} & \leq 0 \\
-x_2 & -x_4 \quad +x_6 + x_7 + x_8 & -x_{11} & \leq 0 \\
x_3 & -x_9 & & \leq 0 \\
-x_3 & +x_9 & & \leq 0 \\
x_5 + x_7 & -x_{10} & & \leq 0 \\
-x_5 - x_7 & +x_{10} & & \leq 0 \\
x_8 + x_9 & -x_{11} - x_{12} & & \leq 0 \\
-x_8 - x_9 & +x_{11} + x_{12} & & \leq 0 \\
x_1 & & & \leq 2 \\
x_2 & & & \leq 7 \\
x_3 & & & \leq 10 \\
x_4 & & & \leq 4 \\
x_5 & & & \leq 6 \\
x_6 & & & \leq 5 \\
x_7 & & & \leq 6 \\
x_8 & & & \leq 3 \\
x_9 & & & \leq 7 \\
x_{10} & & & \leq 13 \\
x_{11} & & & \leq 4 \\
x_{12} & & & \leq 6 \\
x_1, x_2, \cdots, x_{12} & & & \geq 0.
\end{array}
$$

Determine the maximum flow in the network.

16. Determine the maximum flow for the following networks.

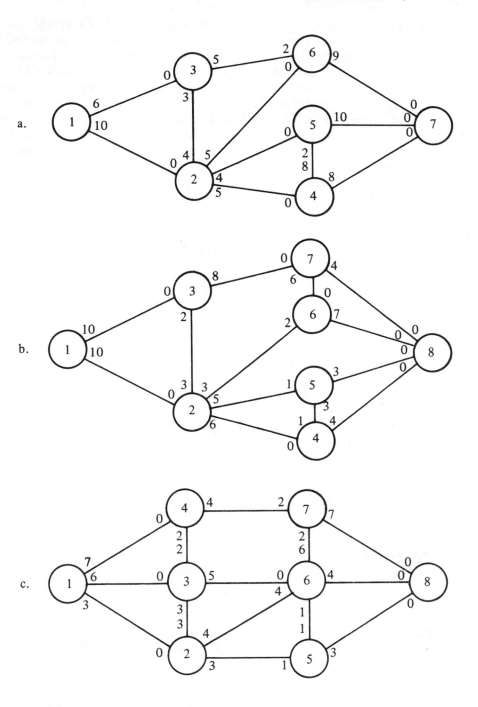

a.

b.

c.

17. A patient is told by his doctor to go on a diet of liver and hamburger. In each meal he must get at least 300 calories from the combination and no more than 21 units of fat. There are 150 calories in a pound of liver, 200 calories in a pound of hamburger, 14 units of fat in a pound of liver and 4 units of fat in a pound of hamburger. Liver costs 30 cents per pound and hamburger 50 cents per pound. Determine the minimum cost meal by graphical means. Note that this problem cannot be formulated as a linear program with a nonnegative right hand side in the constraints, and hence the simplex method as we have described it cannot be used. A more general version of the simplex method, which we have not discussed in this chapter, can handle negative quantities in the right hand side of the constraints and also equalities in the constraints. The interested reader is referred to the further reading at the end of this chapter.

18. The overdetermined system of equations

$$x + y = 3$$
$$x + 2y = 6$$
$$x - y = 0$$
$$2x + 3y = 8$$

cannot be solved exactly. For any values of x, y, we define the residual of each equation to be the difference between the left and right hand sides. Show how the problem of minimizing the largest residual in absolute value can be formulated as a linear programming problem, and determine the values of x and y which achieve this minimum.

Further Reading

Gass, S. I., *Linear Programming,* McGraw-Hill, New York, 1969.

Gue, R. L. and M. E. Thomas, *Mathematical Methods in Operations Research,* Macmillan, New York, 1968.

Hillier, F. S. and G. J. Lieberman, *Introduction to Operations Research,* Holden Day, San Francisco, 1968.

Owen, G., *Game Theory,* W. B. Saunders, Philadelphia, 1968.

Saaty, T. L., *Mathematical Methods of Operations Research,* McGraw-Hill, New York, 1959.

Sasieni, M., A. Yaspan, and L. Friedman, *Operations Research – Methods and Problems,* John Wiley and Sons, New York, 1959.

Spivey, W. A., *Linear Programming – An Introduction,* Macmillan, New York, 1968.

7

Statistics

1. Introduction

Statistics is the science of assembling, analyzing and interpreting collections of data. Statistical methods can be applied in many areas, for example, business, economics, medicine, biology, psychology, physics, education, chemistry, agriculture. It often happens that the amount of data to be handled is quite large, and in these cases a computer is frequently used in the analysis of the data. In this chapter we shall consider various statistical techniques which can be used in data analysis, and describe how these methods can be implemented on a computer. We first define a few statistical terms.

Statistics is concerned with a sample of data from a population. The analysis of this sample is used to make inferences about the population. For example, a company manufacturing light bulbs may wish to estimate the life time of the light bulbs, or an opinion poll may wish to analyze public reaction to a certain candidate in an election. It is impossible to study the life time of every light bulb produced by the company, or to ask every person his views in an election, and hence the statistician will analyze only a fraction of the data.

A population is the totality of objects of a certain class under consideration. People's heights, life times of electric bulbs, voters in an election, automobile accidents, shoe sizes, may all constitute populations of observations.

A sample is a finite number of objects selected from the

population. If these objects are selected in such a manner that one object has as good a chance of being selected as another, we call the sample a random sample. In analyzing the voting patterns of electors, we should not, for example, merely select our sample of voters from just one age group. This sample would not be typical of the entire population and hence would contain a bias. In most cases we make every attempt to obtain a random sample. The statistician will often use a table of random numbers (see Table 5a) to help select a random sample. Statistical characteristics of the sample are used to make inferences about the entire population. The average life time of a sample of 1000 light bulbs, for example, is an indication of the expected life time of all light bulbs produced by the company. Care must be taken, however, when making inferences from a sample, since the sample may be biased or too small for any meaningful conclusions to be drawn. In the following sections we shall consider various techniques which can be used in analyzing samples of data.

Exercises

1. Use the random numbers given in Table 5a to select a random sample of 20 observations from the data given in Table 7a of the next section.

2. Write a computer program to select a random sample of size m from a set of data containing n observations, where m is much smaller than n. Note that care must be taken to avoid repeating observations.

3. Write a computer program to produce a random permutation of the integers 1, 2,3,...,n. (Hint: Store the integers 1, 2,...,n in an integer array of size n. Generate a random integer r between 1 and n inclusive, and interchange the elements in positions 1 and r. Now generate another random integer r between 2 and n inclusive, and interchange the elements in positions 2 and r, and so on.)

2. Frequency Tables and Histograms

In this section we shall consider methods of summarizing data which can be used to extract pertinent information from the data. Table 7a gives the height in inches of a sample of 100 men.

TABLE 7a: Height in inches of a sample of 100 men.

61	64	67	70	70	71	75	72	72	69	68	70	65	67	62	59	62	66	66	68
68	73	71	72	73	71	71	68	69	68	69	65	63	70	70	76	71	72	74	60
56	74	75	79	72	72	69	68	68	68	62	66	66	66	61	77	75	74	63	72
63	62	65	65	66	65	67	67	65	67	68	62	67	60	68	65	70	70	69	70
68	73	64	71	71	68	70	69	73	72	70	69	67	64	67	58	66	69	76	73

It is usually difficult to look at raw data, such as that contained in Table 7a, and get much useful information from it. One method of summarizing data is to construct a frequency table or frequency distribution. This involves dividing the total range of values of the sample into a number of classes, and counting the number of observations which fall into each class. By observing such a table we can readily see the overall pattern of the distribution of our data. An empirical formula which is often used to determine the number of classes is given by

$$K = 1 + 3.3 \log_{10} N \qquad (7.1)$$

where K is the number of classes and N is the size of the sample. In our case $N = 100$ and thus K is given by

$$K = 1 + 3.3 \log_{10} 100 = 1 + 3.3 \times 2 = 7.6$$

This suggests that we use 8 classes. We next look at the data and decide on the class intervals. Referring to Table 7a we see that the smallest value is 56 and the largest 79. This suggests a class width of $(79 - 56)/8 \cong 3$. Thus in the first class we include the values 56, 57, 58, in the second 59, 60, 61, and so on. Note that we are using integers and hence have to be careful in defining the class boundaries. One useful technique is to choose impossible values, for example 55.5–58.5, 58.5–61.5, etc. The frequency table for this data is given in Table 7b.

TABLE 7b: Frequency table for the distribution of the heights of 100 men.

Class interval	Number of observations
55.5 and under 58.5	2
58.5 ” ” 61.5	5
61.5 ” ” 64.5	11
64.5 ” ” 67.5	22
67.5 ” ” 70.5	30
70.5 ” ” 73.5	20
73.5 ” ” 76.5	8
76.5 ” ” 79.5	2

Exercise

4. Write a computer program to produce a frequency table. Assume the data consists of an integer N followed by the N data values of the sample. Your program should use the number of classes K given by

equation (7.1) rounded to the nearest integer. The smallest and largest class boundaries should correspond to the minimum and maximum data values respectively. In each class interval include the lower class boundary but not the upper class boundary, except for the last class interval in which you should include both boundaries.

An alternative method of presenting the frequency distribution of a sample is to make a graphical representation of it. Such a graphical representation is called a histogram. A histogram is very useful since it gives a visual representation of the characteristics of the frequency distribution, and this is often easier to understand than the actual numbers in the frequency table. A histogram is constructed by drawing rectangles on the class intervals so that the areas of the rectangles represent the class frequencies. Note that in the example given in Table 7b, the class widths are all of equal length, and hence the height of the rectangles correspond to the class frequencies. Figure 7a shows a histogram for the frequency distribution given in Table 7b.

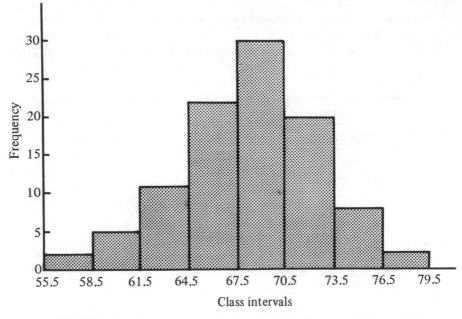

FIGURE 7a: Histogram for the distribution of the heights of 100 men.

Exercises

5. Generate 100 random numbers and draw a histogram using 10 class intervals. What do you expect the histogram to look like?

6. The following table lists the number of pages in a sample of 50

books. Construct a frequency distribution and histogram for this sample.

312	378	345	172	395	214	346	343	145	350
527	330	139	482	496	724	690	607	448	168
332	361	305	313	182	183	138	191	340	132
398	145	418	416	550	350	585	342	171	171
112	434	174	144	165	351	316	468	803	313

7. A pair of dice are thrown 100 times. The following table shows the total score recorded at each throw. Compute the frequency table and draw a histogram. Use 11 class intervals. What do you expect the class frequencies to be?

9	2	7	9	3	6	7	9	3	11	7	3	9	2	6	8	5	8	7	10
9	10	7	9	3	8	8	7	3	11	6	10	7	6	8	7	3	10	6	9
9	6	6	10	5	2	12	7	6	11	11	5	6	2	5	8	7	6	3	9
4	5	6	9	6	10	6	4	6	10	7	9	8	9	4	3	7	4	8	5
11	8	5	4	5	11	6	9	2	4	7	8	7	7	7	4	8	10	6	5

8. Generate a sample of 200 data values where each value is obtained by summing 12 random numbers from the interval (0,1). Construct a frequency table and histogram using 12 class intervals.

3. Descriptive Measures

It is often convenient to summarize data by means of descriptive measures. These measures can be used to indicate the location of the data and also the spread of the data about a central value. The most popular measure of location is the mean.

Given a set of n observations $x_1, x_2,...,x_n$, we define the mean or average to be

$$\bar{x} = \frac{x_1 + x_2 + \cdots + x_n}{n} = \frac{1}{n}\sum x_i. \tag{7.2}$$

(Note that in this and the following sections, wherever a summation sign Σ is written, it is assumed that the summation is taken over all possible values of the observations.) The mean $\bar{x}$ gives an indication of the location of the 'center' of the sample. We are all familiar with batting averages, grade point averages, average monthly rainfall, etc. These are all computed using equation (7.2). For the data given in Table 7a, the mean value $\bar{x}$ is given by

$$\bar{x} = \frac{6820}{100} = 68.20$$

There are two other measures of location which are occasionally used to indicate the centre of a sample.

The median of a set of observations is defined to be the middle number (if it exists). If the number n of observations is odd, then by arranging the data into ascending order, the median is the $(n+1)/2$ observation value. If n is even the median is defined to be midway between the middle two numbers, i.e. to be the value midway between the $(n/2)$ and $(n+2)/2$ observation values. In order to compute the median, it is necessary to sort the data into ascending order. Efficient computer techniques for doing this are discussed in Chapter 9. The median for the data given in Table 7a is 68.

The third measure of location is the mode. The mode is defined as the value which occurs most often. For the data in Table 7a, the value 68 occurs most frequently and hence the mode is 68. Note that a sample may contain more than one mode. In this case it is said to be multimodal.

As well as a measure of location, we also need an indication of the spread of the sample about the center. Referring to Table 7a we see that the maximum and minimum values are 79 and 56 respectively. The range is defined to be the maximum value minus the minimum value. In this case the range is $79 - 56 = 23$. A measure more frequently used is the variance.

Given a set of n observations $x_1, x_2,...,x_n$, we first compute the mean $\bar{x}$ given by equation (7.2). The variance s^2 is then defined by

$$s^2 = \frac{1}{n-1} \left\{ (x_1 - \bar{x})^2 + (x_2 - \bar{x})^2 + \cdots + (x_n - \bar{x})^2 \right\}$$
$$= \frac{1}{n-1} \left\{ \sum (x_i - \bar{x})^2 \right\} . \tag{7.3}$$

The square root of the variance is called the standard deviation and is denoted by s. This gives an indication of the average spread of the sample about the mean. For the data in Table 7a the variance is 19.17 and the standard deviation 4.38. The mean (68.20) and the standard deviation (4.38) are the two descriptive measures most frequently used to summarize data. Notice that for computing purposes equation (7.3) is inefficient, since it involves inspecting the data twice. We first need to scan the data to compute the mean $\bar{x}$, and then re-examine the data to compute the variance s^2. A more efficient (but mathematically identical) formula is given by

$$s^2 = \frac{1}{n-1} \left\{ x_1^2 + x_2^2 + \cdots + x_n^2 - n\bar{x}^2 \right\} .$$

(continued on page 127)

$$= \frac{1}{n-1} \left\{ \sum x_i^2 - n\,\overline{x}^2 \right\}$$

$$= \frac{1}{n-1} \left\{ \sum x_i^2 - \frac{1}{n} \left(\sum x_i\right)^2 \right\} . \qquad (7.4)$$

To compute the variance using equation (7.4) we need only examine the data once and record the sum of the observations and the sum of the squares of the observations. Although equations (7.3) and (7.4) are the same mathematically, they may not give the same answer computationally due to round-off errors. If the observations x_i are all close to the mean $\overline{x}$, then equation (7.3) should be preferred. We note that if the distribution of the data is approximately symmetric, then the median and the mean will be close together. A measure often used to determine the skewness of the data is given by $3(\overline{x} - \text{median})/s$.

A flowchart to compute the mean, variance, and standard deviation of a set of n observations is given in Figure 7b.

Exercises

9. Write a computer program to compute the mean, variance, standard deviation and range of a sample of n observations.

10. Prove that equations (7.3) and (7.4) are mathematically equivalent.

11. Write a computer program to present a complete analysis of a sample of data. Your output should include the raw data, a frequency table with class boundaries and intervals clearly marked, the maximum, minimum and range of the data, and also the mean, variance, and standard deviation. Note that in practice the person inspecting the output may not be a computer expert or a statistician, and hence an elegant clearly labelled layout is desirable.

12. Write a computer program to compute the median of a sample of n observations. Techniques for sorting data are discussed in Chapter 9.

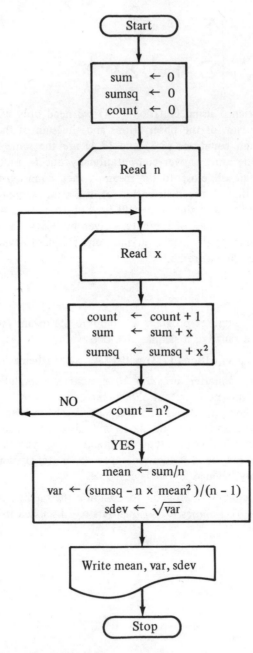

FIGURE 7b: Flowchart to compute mean, variance, and standard deviation.

4. Regression and Correlation

We have so far discussed techniques for analyzing a sample of data which consists of a single observation for each member of the sample. However, the statistician is frequently asked to analyze samples where for each member there may be more than one observation. For example, we may measure both the height and the weight of a sample of individuals. Associated with each individual we would have two measurements (x_i, y_i) corresponding to the height and weight respectively. As a second example, we may wish to analyze the annual profits of a company over a period of years. In this case our data would consist of pairs of measurements (x_i, y_i) where the first measurement is the year, and the second measurement is the corresponding annual profit. We wish to analyze the relationship between these two measurements. The two techniques we shall discuss are correlation and regression.

Table 7c contains the heights and weights of a sample of 14 university professors. The object is to determine if there is any correlation between these two quantities.

TABLE 7c: Heights and weights of 14 men.

Height in inches	Weight in pounds	Height in inches	Weight in pounds
72.9	176.0	73.1	212.3
70.7	152.9	70.5	176.6
71.4	184.1	71.3	133.2
68.5	132.4	72.2	169.5
70.1	161.2	75.0	194.3
68.7	150.6	74.1	178.6
74.0	211.0	69.2	155.1

The first step in the analysis of the data is to draw a scatter diagram. This consists of plotting the pairs of points on a graph (see Figure 7c).

By looking at the graph we see that the points appear to follow a pattern as indicated by the dotted line. This suggests that there is a linear correlation between height and weight. The taller a man is the heavier he is likely to be. The degree of linear correlation between pairs of observations (x_i, y_i) is called the correlation coefficient and is defined by

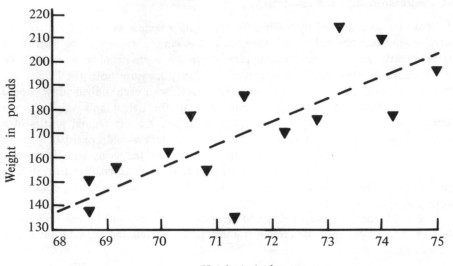

Height in inches

FIGURE 7c: Scatter diagram of height and weight for 14 men.

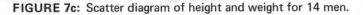

$$r = \frac{\left\{ (x_1 - \bar{x})(y_1 - \bar{y}) + (x_2 - \bar{x})(y_2 - \bar{y}) + \cdots + (x_n - \bar{x})(y_n - \bar{y}) \right\}}{\sqrt{\left\{ (x_1 - \bar{x})^2 + (x_2 - \bar{x})^2 + \cdots + (x_n - \bar{x})^2 \right\} \times \left\{ (y_1 - \bar{y})^2 + (y_2 - \bar{y})^2 + \cdots + (y_n - \bar{y})^2 \right\}}}$$

$$= \frac{\left\{ \sum (x_i - \bar{x})(y_i - \bar{y}) \right\}}{\sqrt{\left\{ \sum (x_i - \bar{x}^2) \right\} \times \left\{ \sum (y_i - \bar{y})^2 \right\}}} . \tag{7.5}$$

Although this formula looks quite complicated mathematically, it is a fairly simple matter to program a computer to evaluate r. If we write equation (7.5) as

$$r = \frac{\frac{1}{n-1} \sum (x_i - \bar{x})(y_i - \bar{y})}{\sqrt{\left\{ \frac{1}{n-1} \sum (x_1 - \bar{x})^2 \right\} \times \left\{ \frac{1}{n-1} \sum (y_i - \bar{y})^2 \right\}}}$$

we see that the denominator is merely the square root of the product of the variance of x and the variance of y. The numerator is called the covariance of x and y and equation (7.5) is often written

$$r = \frac{\text{Cov}(x, y)}{\sqrt{\text{var}(x)\,\text{var}(y)}} . \tag{7.6}$$

It can be shown that the correlation coefficient lies in the range $-1 \leqslant r \leqslant 1$. If r is close to ±1 this suggests a high degree of correlation between the observations. If r is close to zero this suggests that the data is uncorrelated. A positive correlation means that one variable increases as the other increases. For the data given in Table 7c the correlation coefficient = +.76. A negative correlation means that as one variable increases the other decreases. The age of a car and its trade-in value has a negative correlation.

To evaluate the correlation coefficient on a computer we rewrite equation (7.5) as

$$r = \frac{\sum x_i y_i - n\bar{x}\bar{y}}{\sqrt{\left\{\sum x_i^2 - n\bar{x}^2\right\} \times \left\{\sum y_i^2 - n\bar{y}^2\right\}}}$$

$$= \frac{\sum x_i y_i - \frac{1}{n}\sum x_i \sum y_i}{\sqrt{\left\{\sum x_i^2 - \frac{1}{n}(\sum x_i)^2\right\} \times \left\{\sum y_i^2 - \frac{1}{n}(\sum y_i)^2\right\}}}$$

(7.7)

A flowchart of a computer program to evaluate the correlation coefficient r is given in Figure 7d.

Exercises

13. Write a computer program to calculate the correlation coefficient between n pairs of observations (x_i, y_i). Your program should also compute the mean, variance and standard deviation of the x values and the y values.

14. Prove that equations (7.5) and (7.7) are mathematically equivalent.

15. Generate 100 pairs of random numbers and evaluate the correlation coefficient. What do you expect the answer to be?

16. The following table indicates the marks gained by a group of students in Mathematics and English. Is there a correlation between them?

Math	41	67	30	87	25	52	27	10	82	80	45	25	66	47	58
English	37	67	55	42	25	59	70	22	71	57	47	45	46	40	24

17. Prove that $-1 \leqslant r \leqslant +1$. What happens when r = ±1?

In regression analysis we are concerned with determining the best straight line fit to the observations of the sample. Table 7d gives the annual profit of a company in millions of dollars over a period of 10 years. Figure 7e shows a graph of the annual profit plotted against time, and we see that the relationship between these quantities appears to be linear as indicated by the dotted line.

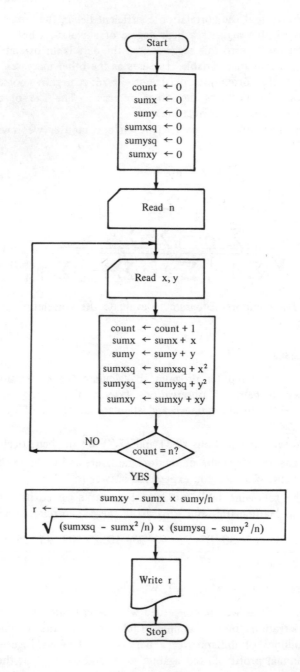

FIGURE 7d: Flowchart to compute the correlation coefficient.

TABLE 7d: Annual profit of a company during a 10 year period.

Year	1	2	3	4	5	6	7	8	9	10
Profit in millions of dollars	1.87	2.19	2.06	2.31	2.26	2.39	2.61	2.56	2.82	2.96

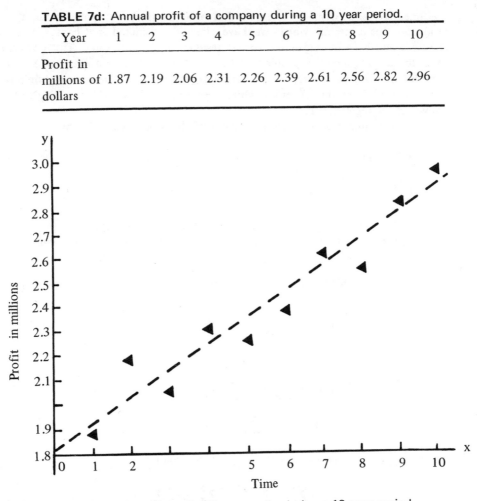

FIGURE 7e: Annual profit of a company during a 10 year period.

We may wish to determine the equation of the straight line which best fits this data according to some specified criterion.

In general we are given a sample of n observations (x_i, y_i) and we wish to determine a straight line of the form

$$\hat{y} = a + bx$$

which closely represents the data. We define the residual at each point x_i to be the observed value y_i minus the straight line value $\hat{y}_i = a + b x_i$. Referring to Figure 7e this is represented by the vertical displacement between a point and the line. We now wish to select a and b to minimize, in some sense, these residuals. One criterion which we have already considered in Chapter 6 is to choose a and b to minimize the largest residual in absolute value. This gives rise to a linear programming problem. The criterion discussed in Chapter 3 is to consider the sum of squares of the residuals, and to choose a and b to minimize this quantity. It is this criterion which we consider here. The resulting line is known as the regression line.

We wish to minimize the sum of squares of the residuals E given by

$$E = \left\{ y_1 - (a + bx_1) \right\}^2 + \left\{ y_2 - (a + bx_2) \right\}^2 + \cdots + \left\{ y_n - (a + bx_n)^2 \right\}$$

$$= \sum \left\{ y_i - (a + bx_i) \right\}^2 . \tag{7.8}$$

Since E is a function of the two variables a and b, we may set the partial derivatives of E with respect to a and b equal to zero. This gives two linear equations in a and b:

$$\sum \left\{ y_i - (a + bx_i) \right\} = 0 \tag{7.9}$$

$$\sum \left\{ y_i - (a + bx_i) \right\} x_i = 0 \tag{7.10}$$

Rewriting, we obtain

$$a\,n + b \sum x_i = \sum y_i \tag{7.11}$$

$$a \sum x_i + b \sum x_i^2 = \sum x_i y_i \tag{7.12}$$

We may solve these two equations analytically, yielding

$$a = \frac{\sum y_i \sum x_i^2 - \sum x_i y_i \sum x_i}{n \sum x_i^2 - (\sum x_i)^2} . \tag{7.13}$$

$$b = \frac{n \sum x_i y_i - \sum x_i \sum y_i}{n \sum x_i^2 - (\sum x_i)^2} . \tag{7.14}$$

Thus, given n observations (x_i, y_i), equations (7.13) and (7.14) give the coefficients a, b of the regression line $\hat{y} = a + bx$ which best fits the data. For the annual profit of the company (Table 7d), the regression line is

$$\hat{y} = 1.811 + 0.108 \, x$$

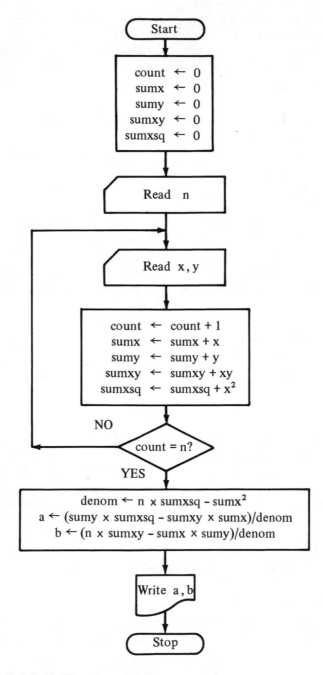

FIGURE 7f: Flowchart for linear regression.

where $\hat{y}$ is the profit and x is the time (see dotted line in Figure 7e).

A flowchart for computing the regression line $\hat{y} = a + bx$ for a set of n observations (x_i, y_i) is given in Figure 7f. The problem of fitting a quadratic or higher degree polynomial to a set of observations is discussed in Chapter 3.

Exercises

18. Show that the solution to equations (7.11) and (7.12) is given by equations (7.13) and (7.14).

19. List several other criteria which might be used in determining the parameters a, b of the straight line. Why do you think the criterion of the sum of squares of the residuals is more commonly used than the largest residual in absolute value?

20. Write a computer program to compute the regression line to a set of n observations (x_i, y_i). Use your program with the data given in Table 7c to determine the ideal weight-height graph.

21. The following table gives the sales of cars by a company over a period of years. Plot a graph of these sales and determine the regression line.

Sales of cars in thousands	53	66	74	82	85	91	92	103
Year	1	2	3	4	5	6	7	8

5. Summary

We have discussed various statistical techniques which can be used in the analysis of data. Usually the calculations associated with these techniques are too laborious to be done by hand, whereas it is a straightforward task to program a computer to perform these calculations. Many computing centers possess standard statistical programs for data analysis. We have not considered ways in which the analysis of a sample can be used to make inferences about the population from which the sample is drawn. This is a very important part of statistics, but a satisfactory treatment of this topic is beyond the scope of this book. Most textbooks on statistics provide ample discussion of this matter.

Exercises

22. The following table gives the life times of 50 electric light bulbs in hundreds of hours. Construct a frequency table and histogram.

15	24	22	9	3	30	12	33	7	18
0	0	27	56	14	17	6	21	13	8
8	9	47	39	16	15	0	1	4	27
11	23	7	2	22	5	3	19	10	1
33	8	32	1	15	12	41	21	15	10

23. The following table lists the waiting times in minutes of 50 patients in a doctor's office. Construct a frequency table and histogram.

14	2	32	5	26	38	30	8	17	0
11	7	24	45	2	5	14	37	22	9
33	53	11	19	16	27	40	20	32	13
18	28	38	20	0	31	29	30	20	27
4	12	45	42	26	23	25	16	21	39

24. Compute the mean, variance, standard deviation and range of the data given in Exercise 22.

25. Compute the median and skewness of the data given in Exercise 23.

26. The following table lists the I.Q. and family size of a group of students. Determine the correlation coefficient between these observations.

I.Q.	97	96	115	76	85	109	100	112	87	89
Family size	4	6	5	7	4	4	5	6	6	7

I.Q.	104	82	102	90	77	78	95	121	118	88
Family size	6	7	3	5	6	5	7	3	4	3

27. The revenue of a book company over a period of years and its earnings per share are given in the following table.

Year	1962	1963	1964	1965	1966	1967	1968	1969
Revenue in thousands of dollars	187.4	281.7	347.5	426.5	449.9	499.6	600.1	858.5
Earnings per share in cents	19	32	33	37	46	53	70	1.10

Determine the correlation coefficient between the earnings and the revenue, and the regression lines for the revenue and the year, and also the earnings and the year.

28. Show how to determine a regression line of the form

$$\hat{y} = bx$$

to a set of n observations (x_i, y_i).

29. A physicist attempts to determine the acceleration due to gravity g, by timing the swing of a pendulum. The time T, and the length of the pendulum L are related by

$$T = 2\pi \sqrt{\frac{L}{g}} \, .$$

The following table lists the outcome of the experiment.

Length of pendulum in feet	2	3	4	5	6	7	8	9	10
Time in seconds	1.55	1.95	2.24	2.46	2.74	2.93	3.17	3.33	3.54

Draw a graph of T plotted against $\sqrt{L}$, and using the regression line of Exercise 28 determine the acceleration due to gravity.

30. Given a set of n observations (x_i, y_i), it is desired to determine an exponential regression curve of the form:

$$\hat{y} = e^{a+bx}$$

This can be accomplished by plotting a graph of log y_i against x_i, and computing the parameters a, b of the linear regression line for this modified data. Determine the parameters of the exponential regression curve to the following data.

x	0	1	2	3	4	5	6	7	8	9
y	2.07	2.63	3.67	4.90	6.71	8.91	12.16	16.33	22.00	29.70

31. The following table gives the population of the world over a period of years.

Year	x	1956	1957	1958	1959	1960	1961	1962
Population in millions	y	2734	2790	2852	2906	2972	3061	3150

Year	x	1963	1964	1965	1966	1967	1968
Population in millions	y	3218	3234	3285	3356	3420	3483

Determine the exponential regression curve of the form

$$\hat{y} = e^{a+bx}$$

which best fits these observations. How many years does it take for the population to double? What does this model predict the population will be in the year 2000?

32. The number of runs and hits scored by the Atlanta Braves over a period of 32 games is given in the following table. Determine the means, variances, covariance and correlation coefficient for these observations.

Runs	0	0	1	0	4	8	2	1	8	9	2	5	12	5	0	6
Hits	2	6	3	5	9	16	6	6	11	12	7	8	17	11	5	10

Runs	11	1	6	5	7	6	8	1	3	5	2	3	5	1	9	8
Hits	17	6	11	8	9	10	16	8	5	6	4	8	6	1	12	12

Further Reading

Dixon, W. J. and F. J. Massey, Jr., *Introduction to Statistical Analysis,* McGraw-Hill, New York, 1969.

Ferguson, G. A., *Statistical Analysis in Psychology and Education,* McGraw-Hill, New York, 1959.

Lohnes, P. R. and W. W. Cooley, *Introduction to Statistical Procedures: with Computer Exercises,* John Wiley, New York, 1968.

Mode, E. B., *Elements of Statistics,* Prentice Hall, New Jersey, 1961.

Smillie, K. W., *An Introduction to Regression and Correlation,* Academic Press, New York, 1966.

C

Data
Processing

What is data processing?

Data processing is a term commonly used to denote the manipulation of business information on a computer. Frequently, however, the term is used when describing all computing of a nonscientific nature or to denote the manipulation of any type of data either with or without a computer. Since the purpose of this text is to introduce the reader to a variety of applications areas in computing, a broad rather than narrow definition of the term data processing is appropriate. Thus, in this text, data processing includes all of those areas where there tends to be more manipulation of data than arithmetic computation. Clearly this definition falls somewhere between the second and third usage of the term given above. Using this definition, data processing not only includes the production of the monthly payroll, the processing of last month's credit card purchases and the handling of airplane reservations, but it also includes the computing done in such diverse areas as natural language translation, symbol manipulation, artificial intelligence, and law enforcement information systems.

In many situations, the space required to store the data in a data processing problem is many times larger than the space required to store the program which manipulates the data. Thus, a person confronted with the task of solving a data processing problem must carefully consider where the data is to be stored. Since the purpose of storing data is to have it readily available for future use, a decision must be made as to how the information will be organized. That is, what data structure will be used. Closely related to this decision is the problem of finding a suitable technique to produce this structure. A method for searching the organized data, to find a required piece of information, must also be devised.

In the four chapters which follow, we introduce many of the problems in data processing and a number of the techniques which are used to solve them. In particular, we describe some of the various storage devices which can be used, discuss a variety of data structures which have been found useful, and suggest various ways for both creating and retrieving data from such structures.

Because of the limited space available and the overall goals of the text, not all topics within the data processing field are discussed in detail. For example, problems in data collection and entry, design of large data bases, and total system design are mentioned but not developed. It is anticipated that the reader who finds the material interesting will naturally take additional courses or consult other references to acquire more knowledge of the subject.

No discussion of data processing would be complete without considering the problem of maintaining an individual's right to privacy and individuality. This problem is becoming one of increasing importance as larger and larger data processing systems are implemented. It is clear that controls of some kind will be needed on the types and extent of information systems, if we are to avoid the world of George Orwell's "1984". Since this text is primarily concerned with introducing the reader to many of the current applications of computers we shall not pursue this topic further. The reader who wishes to consider this problem in more detail should consult the references at the end of Chapter 8.

Basic Data Processing

1. Introduction

As an introduction to a chapter on data processing it is appropriate to give a precise definition of what data processing is. In attempting to do this we observe that every data processing application consists of one or more of the following seven activities.

1. Data Collection: gathering required information.
2. Data Conversion: converting the information into machine usable form.
3. Data Classification: assigning codes which will allow related information to be collected into useful groupings.
4. Data Organization: sorting, or in some other way arranging the data to facilitate processing.
5. Data Evaluation: performing various arithmetical and logical computations in order to obtain further information.
6. Data Storage: saving the original data and computed results for possible future reference.
7. Data Retrieval: providing in a usable form information which is requested.

As the reader has probably noted, each item in the above list includes the word data. What exactly do we mean by this word? Data can be a set of numbers, possibly representing prices, hours, distances or weights. On the other hand it might be a collection of names representing people, places, or things.

145

It might be sentences, addresses, or statements in a FORTRAN, ALGOL, or PL/1 program. Finally, it might be design drawings for a new office block, freeway, or airplane, to mention only a few possibilities. This diversity of possible items which constitute the data in data processing is one of the main reasons for the continual challenge in problem solution in this area of computer science.

Clearly, the above description allows almost anything to be called data processing. In the remainder of this chapter, and the three which follow, we shall attempt to further clarify what data processing is by looking more closely at various aspects of the topic. We begin by giving a brief history of data processing.

2. The Dark Ages (5000 B.C. - 1890 A.D.)

Since antiquity man has collected information of one sort or another. Some of the earliest large collections of data dealt with astronomical phenomena. As commerce developed, various economic records were also kept.

The amount of usable data in these early collections was severely limited by the storage devices used (clay tablets and papyrus scrolls), and by the lack of tools other than fingers and toes to manipulate the information contained on these storage devices.

Man was quick to discover that he was slow at doing computations and prone to make mistakes. Thus he began to devise computational devices to assist in his labors. One of the earliest of these devices was the ancestor of today's abacus. This simple yet effective calculating device is still used extensively throughout Asia and has recently been rediscovered as a useful tool in teaching mathematical skills in the primary grades.

As civilization and commerce developed, so did the need to manipulate more data. Nevertheless, it was not until the year 1642 that Blaise Pascal, at the age of 19, constructed the first mechanical adding machine. The problem which Pascal solved was how to construct a mechanical device to accomplish the "carry" from one column to the next when adding several numbers together. Thus, having relieved himself of the drudgery of adding what seemed like endless columns of figures in his father's tax office, Pascal went on to develop other areas of mathematics including many of the ideas in probability and statistics.

Improbable as it may seem, the next major event in the history of data processing was the adoption of the Constitution of the United States in 1789. In particular, Article 1, Section 2 of that document requires that the representation in the House of Representatives must be proportional to the population of the various states. To guarantee that this was done, a census was to be conducted every ten years and the representation among the various states was to be reallocated as population changes occurred.

Between 1790 and 1880 the United States grew from a country of nearly 4 million people to one of just over 50 million people. During that time little happened to improve data handling processes so that by 1880 a full seven years were required to complete the census computations. With the continued growth of the country it appeared likely that the census of 1890, and certainly that of 1900, would take more than 10 years to complete, thus causing a constitutional crisis. The machines which were devised to avert this crisis were to open a new age in data processing.

Exercises

1. What other historical events could have had an effect on data processing between 5000 B.C. and 1880 A.D.?

2. What did the following men contribute to the development of data processing?

(a) Napier   (c) Felt

(b) Leibnitz   (d) Babbage

3. The Middle Ages (1890 – 1950)

The solution to the 1890 census computation problem was devised by Dr. Herman Hollerith. He adopted the idea of placing the required information on cards. This idea was not completely new, since "instructions" on cards had already been successfully used to drive the Jacquard loom in France nearly two hundred years before. The Englishman, Charles Babbage, had also proposed using card input on his "analytical engine" in the 1830's. Unfortunately, Babbage was a man ahead of his time and some of the precision parts he required could not be manufactured. Because of this, construction of his machine was never completed.

Hollerith, however, devised a code and machines which could punch that code on cards, read the punched cards, and summarize the information on a set of easily read dials. Although crude by today's standards, those first pieces of data processing equipment permitted the 1890 census to be completed in slightly over two years.

Hollerith's first card design, which had round holes and only 45 columns, was used until 1928. In that year, the 80 column card design pictured in Figure 8a was introduced. This card has since become the data processing industry standard.

Each column of the card can contain either a single digit, alphabetic character, or special character such as +, −, *, $, or /. Each character is identified by a unique code represented by a set of holes. Specifically, each of the 80 columns has 12 punch positions as shown in Figure 8b. Thus a card has 12 rows as well as 80 columns.

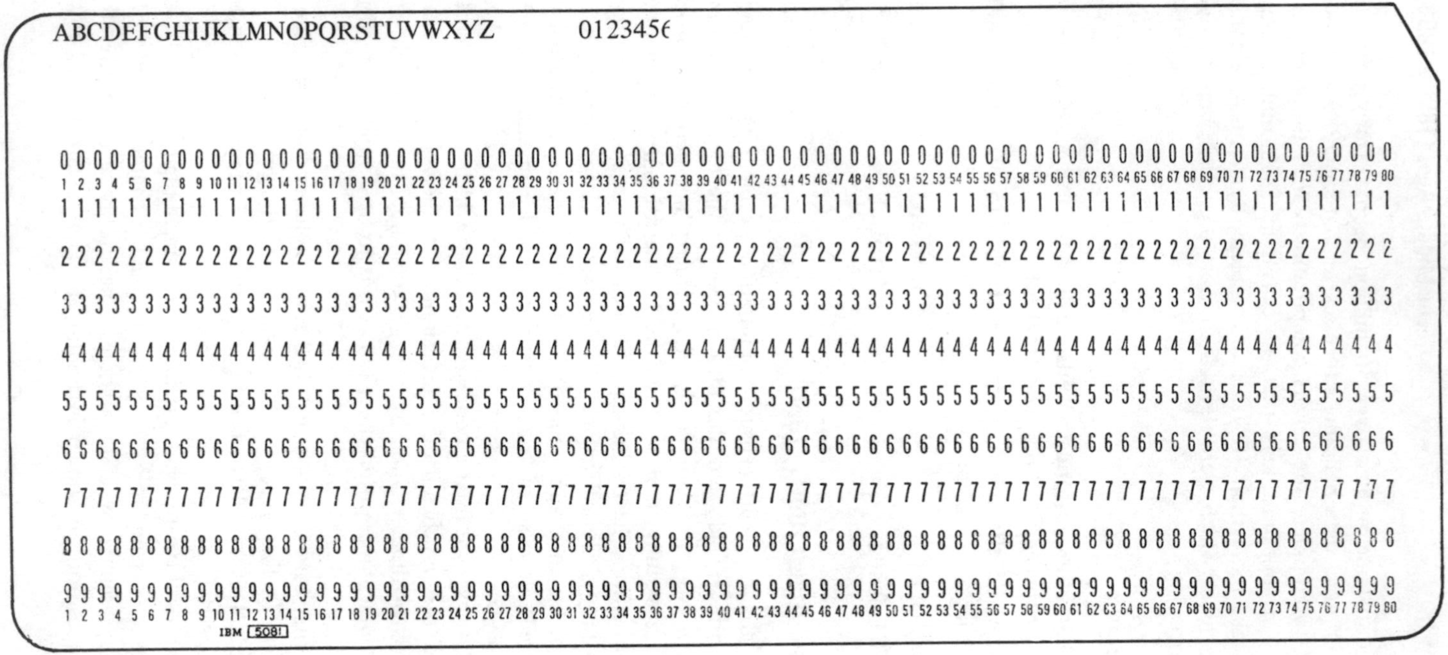

FIGURE 8a: A standard 80 column card.

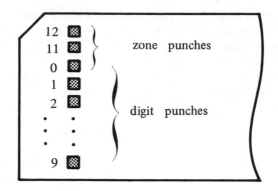

FIGURE 8b: Card punch positions.

A hole in the top row is called a 12 punch, in the second row an 11 punch, in the third row a zero punch, and so on. Also, as indicated in Figure 8b, the top three punch positions are referred to as zone punches while the bottom ten positions are called digit punches. The zero punch can be either a zone or a digit punch. Some of the standard Hollerith codes are given below in Figure 8c.

Character	Zone Punch	Digit Punch
0 - 9	none	0 - 9
A - I	12	1 - 9
J - R	11	1 - 9
S - Z	0	2 - 9

FIGURE 8c: Hollerith card codes.

Special characters have other zone and digit punch combinations.

Since each column on a card can hold only one character, several columns of a card are usually grouped together as the card in Figure 8d illustrates. Thus columns 1−20 are for the student's name, columns 21−50 for the student's address, 51−60 for the student's telephone number, and so on. These groups of

Student Name	Address	Phone	Other
1 - 20	21 - 50	51 - 60	61 - 80

FIGURE 8d: A student record.

columns are called *fields*. Each field contains a single piece of information made up of one or more characters. The collection of pieces of information which describe the given object is usually called a *record*.

A company that wished to keep inventory information on cards might have a card such as that pictured in Figure 8e. This card has fields for the item #, the wholesale price of the item, ..., and finally the number of items in stock. This set of six fields comprises a record of information.

Item #	Wholesale Price	Retail Price	Supplier	Item Name	Number in Stock
1-8	9-15	16-24	25-50	51-70	71-80

FIGURE 8e: An inventory record.

It may be possible to get all the related pieces of information about an item to fit onto one card. For many applications, however, several cards may be required to contain all the related information. The complete set of information is still called a record. The information which will fit on a single card is commonly called a *unit record*.

Since the machines which were developed to handle cards could process only one card at a time they came to be called unit record machines and the cards are often called unit record cards.

Obviously, in any real situation we would have a number of records, one for each item of interest to us. This set of records is called a *file*. Thus the card in Figure 8e would be one record in an inventory file while the card of Figure 8d would be part of a student file.

Files are considered to be of two types, sequential and random. If a file is being considered as a sequential file then we look at each record in sequence. That is, if we are looking at the nth record in the file now we will look at the (n + 1)st record next. If a file is being used as a random file, however, it is not necessary to look at the records sequentially. Thus, if we are looking at the nth record in a random file now, it is possible to look at any record in the file next.

By the middle of the 1930's unit record equipment had developed to the point where the following devices were available:

Key punches — for entering data into cards.

Verifiers — for checking that the correct data was entered into the cards.

Sorters — for arranging the cards in alphabetical or numerical order.

Collators — for merging several sorted decks into a single sorted deck.

Alphabetic accounting machines — which could read cards containing both alphabetic and numeric data, do simple operations such as adding and subtracting and print the results.

Thus, in 1936, it was possible for the federal government of the United States to implement its Social Security system. This was no small task as it initially required setting up accounts for approximately 30 million people. Before the end of the first full year of operation over 1 million accounts were being handled daily. Coverage under the Social Security system has expanded steadily and today well over 125 million accounts are handled using both unit record equipment and computers. This is one of the largest single data processing operations in the world.

During the period from the middle 1930's to the present, the speed and capabilities of unit record equipment have continued to improve. Thus many businesses still rely on this type of equipment instead of more expensive and sophisticated computing equipment.

Exercises

3. Figure 8e shows an inventory record for a hypothetical company. Explain what you think would happen if you bought all of item #2316 which that company had in stock.

4. How would you keep track of records which require more than one card?

5. Using a telephone book as a reference, determine how many columns on a card are needed to store a last name and two initials.

6. How much space would be required to store a street address?

7. If a stack of 2000 cards is about 15 inches high, how high would a stack of 125 million cards be? How does this compare with the height of Mt. Everest?

8. What type of information would you expect to find in a Social Security record?

4. The Advent of Computers

Although Dr. Vannevar Bush completed the first analog computer in 1930, it was not until late in the 1930's and early in the 1940's that large numbers of these devices were built. Designed on the principle of finding a physical analogue of the problem to be solved, these computers were used extensively for gunnery guidance systems and other computational purposes. Although well suited to solving certain mathematical problems where only limited accuracy is required, analog computers are not suitable for most data processing applications because of their inability to handle non-numeric data and their limited precision. Modern data processing had to wait for the digital computer.

It was not until 1944 that the first digital computer, Mark I, was produced at Harvard University. During the next few years a number of computers with exotic names like ENIAC and EDSAC were designed and built in North America and Europe. These were all one of a kind machines. Many of the ideas, however, which were pioneered on these machines were to appear in 1951 and 1952 on the first "mass produced" computers.

The growth of the computing industry since then can only be described as phenomenal. Starting from only a handful of computers in 1951, the industry has grown so that there are now estimated to be between 90,000 and 100,000 computers in operation throughout the world. The total investment in such equipment exceeds 20 billion dollars.

As would be expected, early computers relied heavily on cards. Initially both the instructions and data to be manipulated were read from cards since the computer had no memory. It was soon realized that to achieve the full capability of the new computers some other means of storing the program and the data to be manipulated were necessary. The basic problem was one of speed. While even the earliest computers could perform several thousand computations per second, the best card readers were only able to supply a few hundred characters per second to manipulate. The obvious solution was to provide other memory devices to hold both the data and the program. One of the major reasons for the rapid expansion of computing facilities has been the ability of scientists and engineers to meet this challenge. They have devised a variety of ways of storing large quantities of information in forms which computers can recognize and manipulate quickly. Space limitations will not permit us to describe every memory device which is currently available. It does seem appropriate, however, to consider the characteristics of the main memory of a computer. Tape and disk memories will also be described since they are the most widely used auxiliary memory devices.

Exercises

9. Ohm's law states that $V = I \times R$ where V is the voltage drop when an electrical current I flows through a resistance R. Explain how this law might be used to construct an analog computer to do multiplications and divisions.

10. Have a friend write down 10 addition problems each involving two numbers with from 3 to 8 digits in each number. Time how many seconds it takes you to complete all the additions. Assuming that each

addition would require 4 machine operations (loading the first number into the arithmetic unit, loading the second number into the arithmetic unit, adding the two numbers, and storing the answer back in memory), how many times faster is the computer you are using than you?

5. Storage Devices

(a) Main memory

In order for a computer to work at speeds which may range from several thousand instructions per second on slow machines to over a million instructions per second on fast machines, it is necessary that both data and instructions are available in a storage device which can match these speeds. The main memory of the computer fulfills this requirement.

The main memory of a computer consists of a number of *storage locations*. Each storage location has a unique address and the computer has the ability to determine what the contents of any particular storage location are, simply by supplying the address of the given location to its control unit. The amount of information which can be stored in a given storage location depends upon the design of the computer. In some machines each addressable location is just large enough to store a single character. In others, as many as six or eight characters can be stored in a single storage location. The number of characters that can be stored in a location is determined by the number of *bits* (**b**inary dig**its**) in the storage location.

A binary digit is a number which is either 0 or 1. Thus a computer with 8 bit storage locations might contain any of the bit combinations shown in Figure 8f.

$$
\begin{array}{cccccccc}
0 & 0 & 0 & 0 & 0 & 0 & 0 & 0 \\
0 & 0 & 1 & 0 & 0 & 1 & 0 & 1 \\
0 & 1 & 0 & 1 & 1 & 1 & 1 & 1 \\
1 & 0 & 1 & 1 & 0 & 0 & 0 & 0 \\
1 & 1 & 1 & 1 & 1 & 1 & 1 & 1
\end{array}
$$

FIGURE 8f: Some possible 8 bit combinations.

A natural way to look at a string of binary digits is to think of it as a binary (base 2) number. Since the reader may not be familiar with binary numbers we will take a moment to explain them.

When we write the number six thousand three hundred and forty-seven using decimal digits we write 6347 and we mean

6 x ten cubed + 3 x ten squared + 4 x ten + 7

because we are working in base ten. That is, we have only the ten digits 0, 1,

2,...,9 with which to represent our number. Now, if we have only the two digits 0 and 1 with which to work we have a base two number system. Thus, when we write the number 1011 we mean

$$1 \text{ x two cubed} + 0 \text{ x two squared} + 1 \text{ x two} + 1$$

which is eleven.

In Figure 8g we give the numbers from zero to fifteen in both their base ten and base two notations.

Base 10	Base 2
0	0000
1	0001
2	0010
3	0011
4	0100
5	0101
6	0110
7	0111
8	1000
9	1001
10	1010
11	1011
12	1100
13	1101
14	1110
15	1111

FIGURE 8g: Binary representation of the numbers from zero to fifteen using 4 bits.

It should be fairly obvious to the reader that given enough bits we could store any integer in the computer. It is then only necessary to have some instructions which will tell the computer to do arithmetic operations on the numbers and computation may begin.

Storage of character data is not much more difficult. Recalling that alphabetic characters are stored in cards using a zone and a digit punch, we might adopt the storage convention pictured in Figure 8h. Thus each alphabetic character would be stored in 8 bits, A as 11000001,, B as 11000010,..., and Z as 10101001. Sometimes we wish to treat digits as characters also. It is then necessary that an appropriate character code, possibly different from its numerical code, be used. Depending on the total number of characters allowed we may not need 8 bits to distinguish them. Table 8a lists the standard 6 bit and 8 bit character codes in use today.

Character	Card Form		Machine Form	
	zone	digit	zone	digit
A - I	12	1 - 9	1100	0001 - 1001
J - R	11	1 - 9	1011	0001 - 1001
S - Z	0	2 - 9	1010	0010 - 1001

FIGURE 8h: A possible machine representation for alphabetic characters using 8 bits.

TABLE 8a: Standard 6 bit and 8 bit character codes.

Character	BCD code	EBCDIC code	ASCII code
blank	110 000	0100 0000	0100 0000
.	011 011	0100 1011	0100 1110
(	111 100	0100 1101	0100 1000
+	010 000	0100 1110	0100 1011
$	101 011	0101 1011	0100 0100
*	101 100	0101 1100	0100 1010
)	011 100	0101 1101	0100 1001
—	100 000	0110 0000	0100 1101
/	110 001	0110 0001	0100 1111
,	111 011	0110 1011	0100 1111
'	001 100	0111 1101	0100 0111
=	001 011	0111 1110	0101 1101
A	010 001	1100 0001	1010 0001
B	010 010	1100 0010	1010 0010
C	010 011	1100 0011	1010 0011
D	010 100	1100 0100	1010 0100
E	010 101	1100 0101	1010 0101
F	010 110	1100 0110	1010 0110
G	010 111	1100 0111	1010 0111
H	011 000	1100 1000	1010 1000
I	011 001	1100 1001	1010 1001
J	100 001	1101 0001	1010 1010
K	100 010	1101 0010	1010 1011
L	100 011	1101 0011	1010 1100
M	100 100	1101 0100	1010 1101
N	100 101	1101 0101	1010 1110

(continued)

Character	BCD code	EBCDIC code	ASCII code
O	100 110	1101 0110	1010 1111
P	100 111	1101 0111	1011 0000
Q	101 000	1101 1000	1011 0001
R	101 001	1101 1001	1011 0010
S	110 010	1110 0010	1011 0011
T	110 011	1110 0011	1011 0100
U	110 100	1110 0100	1011 0101
V	110 101	1110 0101	1011 0110
W	110 110	1110 0110	1011 0111
X	110 111	1110 0111	1011 1000
Y	111 000	1110 1000	1011 1001
Z	111 001	1110 1001	1011 1010
0	000 000	1111 0000	0101 0000
1	000 001	1111 0001	0101 0001
2	000 010	1111 0010	0101 0010
3	000 011	1111 0011	0101 0011
4	000 100	1111 0100	0101 0100
5	000 101	1111 0101	0101 0101
6	000 110	1111 0110	0101 0110
7	000 111	1111 0111	0101 0111
8	001 000	1111 1000	0101 1000
9	001 001	1111 1001	0101 1001

In order for the computer to handle the character data it must be given additional instructions. It is then the responsibility of the programmer to see that character handling instructions are used where characters are stored and number handling instructions are used where numbers are stored. This is because the computer by itself cannot tell what the bits stand for. For example, the string of bits 11000101 could stand for the letter E or for the number 197 depending on the interpretation (character or numeric) used.

The reader has no doubt been wondering just how the bits are stored in the computer. Their actual representation depends on the type of memory device involved, i.e., magnetic core, magnetic drum, thin film, or monolithic, to mention a few. Because of their wide use, we shall describe how bits are stored using magnetic cores. On many computers the main memory is called *core storage*. This is because it consists of thousands, and in some cases millions, of small ferro-magnetic rings, called *cores*. Looking much like a doughnut, only many times smaller, each core can be magnetized in a clockwise or counter clockwise direction. As Figure 8i suggests, it is easy to associate one magnetic orientation with 0 and the other with 1.

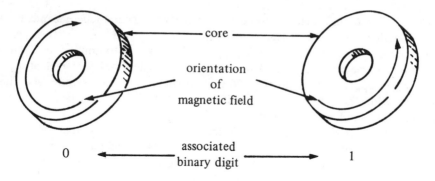

FIGURE 8i: Magnetic cores.

By stringing several wires through the hole in the core it is possible to set the core to either value 0 or 1 by passing a small current through the wires. It is also possible to determine the present value in the core by detecting the small current generated when the core reverses its magnetic orientation. A storage location consists of a set of these cores.

The main memory of a computer has two very desirable characteristics. First, it is fast. It can provide information to the computer at the maximum rate that the computer can manipulate the data. Secondly, it has the capability of random access. This means, for example, that having used the data in location 722 we can then get the data from location 17324, and then the data from location 8359, simply by specifying these addresses in turn to the control unit. In this way there is no need to look at intermediate locations which are not of immediate interest.

Unfortunately, providing both speed and random access is expensive. Thus it is no surprise that there is only a limited amount of main memory available on any given computer. For most data processing applications there will not be enough of this main memory to hold both the program and all of the data to be manipulated. Because of this we are forced to use some sort of auxiliary storage device to hold most of the data.

(b) Magnetic tape

Magnetic tape is probably the most commonly used auxiliary storage device available today. The tape itself is a strip of plastic material which is coated with iron oxide. It is similar to the tapes found on tape recorders except that it is wider, heavier, and is used in longer lengths. A tape reel may contain anywhere from 50 to 2400 feet of tape, the latter length being the most common.

Information is stored on the tape by magnetizing a set of spots in the iron oxide. A code similar to that used in storing information in main memory is used.

The amount of information stored on a piece of magnetic tape depends both on its length and on the character density. Since it is possible to store up to 1600 characters per inch, it would appear that about 40 million characters (500,000 unit record cards) could be stored on a single 2400 foot reel of tape. Actually the upper limit is closer to 20 million characters (see Exercise 14). This compares with the largest main memories currently available which will hold approximately 4 million characters.

Input of information from tapes is many times faster than that of a card reader. For example, the typical 1000 card per minute card reader can supply a computer with only about 1333 characters per second while a typical tape unit can supply between 20,000 and 200,000 characters per second, depending on how fast the tape is moving past the read/write heads on the tape drive and how many characters per inch are stored on the tape. With these speeds, if the data being manipulated can be placed on the tape so that the next piece of information to be needed is the next piece of data on the tape, then the computer will be able to run at full or nearly full speed. If the data is scattered throughout the tape, however, there will be much wasted time due to waiting for the tape to move to the item wanted next. The worst possible case would occur if the program using the tape needed the first piece of data on the tape and then the last piece of data on the tape. In such a situation, it would be necessary to wait for up to 2400 feet of tape to run through the tape drive. This would require about 4 minutes.

In using tapes, five different operations are usually available. First we can write on the tape. Since there are usually several tape drives available we must specify the tape drive number and also give a list of the quantities to be written on the tape on that drive. We shall denote this operation by "WRITE TAPE #, list." The information placed on the tape by each WRITE TAPE command is called a record.

Having loaded the tape with information it would look something like the tape pictured in Figure 8j. Notice that the records are not necessarily all of the same length. This will depend on how many items there are in the "list" each

Start of tape   End of tape

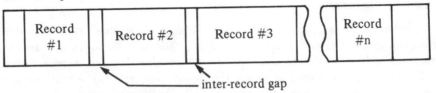

inter-record gap

FIGURE 8j: Typical tape.

time we write. Also note that there is some space between each record on the tape. This is the starting and stopping space required by the tape drive. It is usually about 3/4 of an inch long and is called the inter-record gap. Just as with cards, the set of records on the tape is called a file.

Once we have loaded a tape with data we may want to use some of the data. To start at the beginning of the tape a rewind instruction is used. We denote this instruction by "REWIND #." This causes the specified tape to be repositioned at its start. Any time we have a program in which tapes are used we issue a rewind instruction before any other instructions involving the tape are used. This is to make certain that we are starting at the front of the tape since the computer operator may not have positioned it there when it was mounted.

To use the information on a tape we must read it from the tape back into main memory. We will denote this operation by "READ TAPE #, list." Enough information is read from the tape to assign each item in the list a value. If the length of the record which we read is not the same length as the record on the tape, an error message is usually given. Just as in the main memory, reading information from the tape does not change either the information that was read or any of the other information stored on the tape.

When reading records from a tape we may or may not know exactly how many records there are. In order to avoid reading past the end of the file it is usually possible to write a special record called an *end of file mark*. If this record is read while attempting to read some other record a suitable error message is printed or the program is notified that it has come to the end of the file and is allowed to take suitable action. We shall denote the command to write the end of file record by "END FILE #."

It often happens that having moved part way through a tape we want to look at some information which we have already read but for some reason is no longer available to us in main memory. This can be accomplished by asking the tape drive to backspace. This will cause the tape drive to move the tape so that the read/write head is positioned at the $(n-1)$st record from the front of the tape if they were previously at the nth record from the front. Repeated application of this command could take us back to the front of the tape. We shall denote this operation by "BACKSPACE #."

One final comment about tapes is necessary. Unlike main memory we cannot write a new record in the middle of a file stored on most tapes and expect to be able to still get at the last half of the file. This holds true even if the new record apparently is of the same length as the one it replaces. The problem lies in the fact that the tape drive may run at slightly different speeds at different times due to power fluctuations and this can mean that slightly more or slightly less space is used to store the information on the tape. This in turn could mean that the resulting inter-record gap was too small or that an extra inter-record gap with part of the old record could be left in the middle of the file. In either case we would have lost access to the last part of the file. Because of this, we must copy the complete tape onto a new tape if we wish to make any changes in the information. The one exception would be if we are writing new records at the end of a file. Of course, once the information on a tape is of no further use to us we can simply write new information on that tape and this destroys anything previously written there.

(c) Magnetic disk storage

Next to magnetic tape, magnetic disk storage is the most widely used auxiliary storage device today. As the name inplies, a magnetic disk is a flat circular disk which is coated with iron oxide. Except that there are no grooves on the surface, it has an appearance much like that of a phonograph record. Several of these disks are stacked on top of each other with a small separator between each of them to form what is called a *disk pack* such as that pictured in Figure 8k. When the disk is to be used it is mounted on a disk drive. The disk drive contains a motor which causes the disk pack to rotate at a constant speed of 1200 revo-

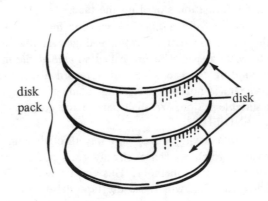

disk pack

disk

FIGURE 8k: A disk pack.

lutions per minute. The drive also contains a set of read/write heads, see Figure 8l, which can move in and out between the disks as they rotate. These heads can either place information on a disk or read information from a disk as it rotates past where they are located. As with magnetic tape, the information is stored using magnetized spots. The amount of information stored on a single disk pack depends on how many disks are involved but it can range from several million to 400 million characters.

To facilitate storage and retrieval of information from a disk pack each disk surface has its own number, 0, 1, 2, 3,...,l, where l depends on the number of disks in the pack. Each disk is divided into a set of concentric circular tracks on

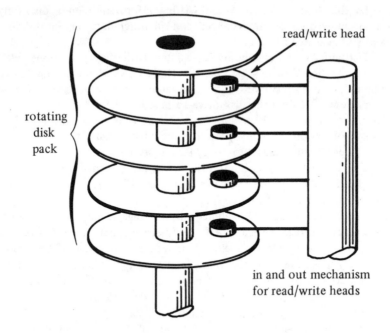

FIGURE 8l: Typical disk drive configuration.

which the information is stored. Each track has a unique number ranging from 0 to m. See Figure 8m. Each track in turn is divided into sectors numbered from 0 to n. When we wish to place information on a disk or read information from a disk we specify which disk, track, and sector. When reading information none of

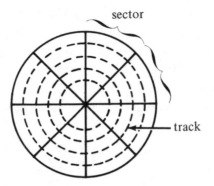

FIGURE 8m: Disk surface.

the data on the disk is altered. When writing information on a disk only the sectors actually written on are changed and all other data on the disk is unaffected and still available for later use.

Three instructions are commonly associated with disk operations. We shall denote them by "READ DISK (l,m,n)," "WRITE DISK (l,m,n)," and "SEARCH (m)," where l, m, n specify the disk, track and sector respectively. The search instruction allows us to tell the disk drive to position the read/write heads over a particular track on all the disks in the pack some time before we actually do a read or write operation. This instruction is included because the time it takes to position the read/write heads (up to 1/4 of a second) is much larger than the actual reading or writing time. Some disk drives are designed with an individual read/write head for every track on every surface. Clearly, the search operation would not be needed in that case.

As the reader has no doubt concluded, disk storage is quite suitable for use as a random access storage device since any piece of data chosen from several million can be found in 1/4 of a second or less. In particular, if the read/write head is already positioned on the right track the average waiting time is only 1/40th of a second. Disk storage can of course also be used for sequential storage of data. When used in this way it can provide data to the computer at up to twice the rate provided by magnetic tape.

In this section we have described only two of the many auxiliary memory devices which are currently available. This is not meant to imply that magnetic drums, magnetic cards, or punched paper tape, to mention only a few of the currently available alternatives, should not be considered when setting up a real data processing system. Clearly the needs of the system and the relative costs of satisfying those needs with various types of hardware should be a major factor in deciding which memory devices are actually used.

Exercises

11. Represent each of the following binary numbers as decimal numbers.

(a)	1010	(d)	11011011
(b)	11010	(e)	1010101
(c)	10011	(f)	11001101010

12. Represent the following decimal numbers in base two..

(a)	16	(d)	86
(b)	19	(e)	329
(c)	24	(f)	73216

13. The addition and multiplication tables for binary numbers are given

below. Use them to compute each of the following expressions:

+	0	1
0	0	1
1	1	10

Binary addition table

x	0	1
0	0	0
1	0	1

Binary multiplication table

(a) 1111   (b) 1011   (c) 1010   (d) 1101
  + 101   +1011   x 101   x1011

14. How many records (characters) could we store on a 2400 foot reel of tape if the recording density is 1600 characters per inch and

   (a) each record contains 100 characters?
   (b)   ”   ”   ”   200 characters?
   (c)   ”   ”   ”   400 characters?
   (d)   ”   ”   ”   800 characters?
   (e)   ”   ”   ”   1600 characters?

15. If we have just read the 18th record on a tape how many backspaces must we take if we wish to read the 17th record again?

6. Data Processing Examples

In concluding this chapter it is appropriate that we consider in some detail several typical data processing problems. The two problems most commonly associated with business data processing are payroll and inventory control. The first is normally handled using a sequential file while the second is probably handled best using a random access file.

(a) A payroll problem

ABC Manufacturing keeps records of all employees and wages paid to them so that the appropriate income tax declaration slips can be produced at the end of each year. This information is stored in a *master file* on magnetic tape. Each record in the file contains, among other things, the following pieces of information about an individual employee: the employee's name (NAME); the employee identification number (MSTRID); pay rate (PRATE); cumulative gross pay to date in current year (CUMPAY); cumulative pension plan deductions in current year (CUMPEN); number of exemptions (NOEXMP); and cumulative income tax deductions in current year (CUMTAX). We will assume that this master file is sorted into ascending order by the employee identification number.

Each week the accounting department of ABC manufacturing prepares a *weekly transaction file* from the previous week's time cards. This file is punched on unit record cards. Each card contains an employee number (CARDID) and the number of hours worked during the previous week (WEEKHR) by that employee. Once the weekly transaction file has been sorted into ascending order by the employee number, using a card sorter, it is used to update the master file and produce a pay check for the employee.

We will assume that the last record both in the master file and in the weekly

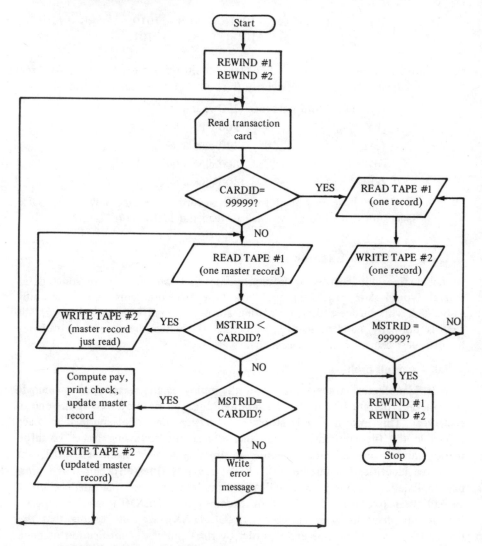

FIGURE 8n: Payroll flowchart.

transaction file is a dummy record with identification number 99999. We also will assume that the old master file is on tape drive #1 and that the updated master file is to be written onto the tape on drive #2. Figure 8n gives a flow chart for a program to update the file and print the pay checks. Some explanation of the flow chart is probably in order.

We begin by rewinding the tapes on tape drives 1 and 2. This guarantees that we are starting at the beginning of both tapes and hence will not miss any records when we read the tape on drive 1 or have any unwanted information in front of the records we write on the tape on tape drive 2. Having rewound the tapes we are ready to read a card from the transaction file and ask if it is the last card. If it is, we copy the remainder of the records on tape 1 onto tape 2, rewind the tapes so that they can be placed back in the tape storage racks, and end the program. If the card read from the transaction file is not the last card then we begin to search the old master file for the master record which matches the current card number (CARDID). Since the master file and the transaction file are both sorted, one of three things can happen. First, the identification number read from the master file (MSTRID) can be smaller than CARDID. This could happen if an employee does not work for the company any longer so that some identification numbers on the master file are not present in the transaction file. In this case we must place the old master record in the new master file and continue searching for the master record we desire. Second, the two numbers could be the same. In this case we must alter some of the information in the old master record, place the resulting record in the new master file, print a pay check, and then get a new card from the transaction file. Finally, the identification number read from the master file might be larger than CARDID. This means that an error has been made. Either the cards have not been sorted properly, a key punch error has been made on a transaction card producing a nonexistant employee identification number, or a new employee has started to work for the company and a master file entry has not as yet been provided for him. In any of these cases we stop the program until the input data or master file has been corrected.

Although we have made a good start, it should be obvious to the reader that before the flow chart in Figure 8n can be used as the basis for a real payroll processing program, there are a number of loose ends which would need to be taken care of. In particular, records of income tax withheld, pension withheld, and total wages paid would need to be produced. Other problems which confront the programmer include the fact that some employees are paid on an hourly basis while others are salaried (paid a fixed amount each week), some employees have union dues deducted once a month while others do not. Possibly the reader can think of other problems not handled by the above flowchart.

(b) An inventory problem

XYZ Groceries has a large warehouse which services a number of retail outlets. Each evening, the store managers phone in orders for delivery to their stores the following day. All orders must be processed before 11:00 p.m. so that loading bills can be delivered to the warehouse floor by midnight when order filling and truck loading begins. Because of this it is not possible to sort all the orders before they are processed. For this reason it was decided to store the master inventory records on a random access disk file rather than on magnetic tape.

We will assume that the disk pack being used has ten surfaces, that each surface has 200 tracks, and that each track is divided into 100 sectors. We shall also assume that an inventory master record will fit in a single sector. Each master record consists of the following quantities: item name (ITNAME); wholesale price (WPRICE); retail price (RPRICE); current number of items in stock (INVENT); reorder level (RLEVEL); supplier (SUPPLY); reorder quantity (RQUANT); reorder indicator (RIND). For simplicity, we will also assume that each inventory item is given a 3 part item number which corresponds to the disk, track, and sector on which it is located in the master file. Only track numbers 50 to 99 are valid for inventory information since the other tracks contain other files.

The daily transaction file for each store consists of a header card, which identifies the requesting store, followed by a set of cards each of which contains a 3 part item number (L, M, N) and the quantity of that item ordered (IORDER). The end of the daily transaction file for a given store is identified by a card with IORDER equal to zero. The end of the complete daily transaction file is identified by a header card with no store name. The flowchart in Figure 8o shows how the daily transaction file can be processed.

A few comments about the flowchart are appropriate. Having read a card we immediately issue a SEARCH command so that the read/write heads on the disk can be positioning themselves while the computer verifies that the card just read is not the end of a store's file and that the item number requested is within the allowable range. As noted before, this will reduce the waiting time on the READ DISK instruction if we must switch tracks. Having found the required master record, we must check that there is enough stock in inventory to meet the request. If insufficient stock is present, only the stock available is supplied. Having printed the invoice we must determine if the remaining stock in inventory has fallen below some specified reorder level (RLEVEL). If it has, the warehouse must itself place an order for another RQUANT of the item from its supplier. However, if the reorder indicator RIND indicates that a reorder has already been placed then we skip the reorder step.

As with the payroll problem there are a number of features which are not included in the flow chart in Figure 8o which would probably be included in an

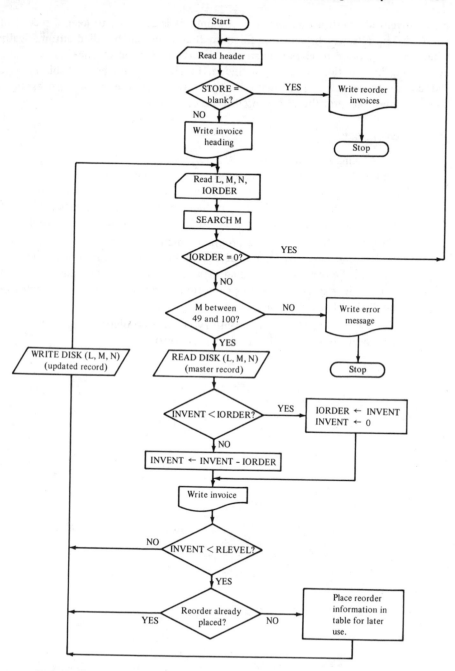

FIGURE 8o: Inventory control flow chart.

actual inventory control program. For example, it is desirable to keep a record of all stock requests which were not filled so that they can be filled automatically when the warehouse receives new stock. Also the collection of sales statistics and accounting information is usually included. Finally, it might be desirable to have the computer sort the input data in the transaction file before processing a store's requests so that the disk is used more efficiently.

Exercises

16. A single input error causes termination of the program given in Figure 8n and thus the possibility that paychecks will not be ready in time. Draw a new flow chart which will find the correct master record if the transaction file has been improperly sorted. An error message should be printed and processing continued if a master record cannot be found.

17. Draw a flowchart for a program which would update the master file used in the payroll problem of Figure 8n. Assume that updating of the file can be caused by adding new employees to the payroll or by changes in pay rates due to promotions. Can both kinds of updates be handled at the same time?

18. The flowchart for the inventory control problem in Figure 8o could have been drawn as follows: (see page 169)

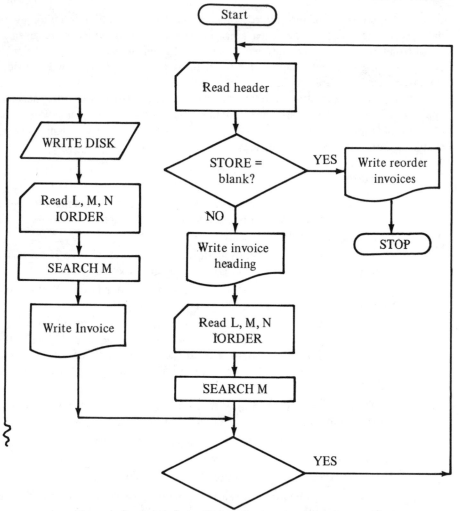

(remainder same as in Figure 80 except print removed)

What would be the advantage of this program over that given in Figure 80?

19. Draw a flowchart for the inventory control problem assuming that each store's requests are sorted and that the inventory records are kept on tape. You may assume that "READ TAPE K, list" means read the tape on drive 1 or 2 depending on whether K currently has the value 1 or 2 in the program and similarly for "WRITE TAPE K, list" "REWIND K," etc.

7. Summary

In this chapter we have introduced some of the basic ideas and terminology of data processing. Each of the seven areas of data processing which were given in the introduction to this chapter have been considered at least briefly, particular attention being given to items 2 and 6. In subsequent chapters we will consider the other items in more detail.

Although the examples given in this chapter are taken only from business applications, the reader should not conclude that this is the only area where the ideas of data processing apply. In the chapters which follow we shall consider problems from other applications areas.

Exercises

20. Once an inventory control system has been implemented on a computer, will it ever be necessary to compare actual inventory levels with computer levels? Explain.

21. Once income tax declaration slips have been produced is it necessary to keep the master file in the payroll program? Explain.

22. If a library decides to store all its records about books (both in and out) on a computer, how would you suggest they do it?

23. One of the problems associated with the flowchart in Figure 8n was the possibility that the input data was not in sequence. Modify the flowchart in Figure 8n to provide sequence checking of all the input before any of the pay checks are produced or a new master file is created.

24. Design a data processing system for an oil company which wishes to send monthly statements to its credit card holders.

25. Determine how +, −, and ÷ are done on an abacus.

26. Determine how Pascal's adder works.

27. Construct an analog computer based on Ohm's law.

28. Early computers used memories consisting of relay switches or tubes such as are found in older radios. Explain how these can be used to hold bits of information.

29. What are the physical characteristics of magnetic drums; of bulk core; paper tape?

30. What did each of the following men contribute to the development of digital computers?

    (a)   Howard Aiken

    (b)   John von Neumann

Further Reading

Brooks, F. P. and Iverson, K. E., *Automatic Data Processing,* John Wiley, New York, 1963.

Clark, F. J., *Information Processing,* Goodyear Publishing Co., Pacific Palisades, Calif., 1970.

Colbert, D. A., *Data Processing Concepts,* McGraw-Hill, New York, New York, 1968.

Crawford, F. R., *Introduction to Data Processing,* Prentice-Hall, Englewood Cliffs, New Jersey, 1968.

Elliot, C. O. and R. S. Wasley, *Business Information Processing,* Richard D. Irwin, Inc., Homewood, Illinois, 1965.

Gear, C. W., *Computer Organization and Programming,* McGraw-Hill, New York, 1969.

Hoffman, L. J., "Computers and Privacy: A Survey," *Computing Surveys,* Vol. 1, No. 2 (June), 1969.

Phillips, G. M. and P. J. Taylor, *Computers,* Methuen and Company Ltd., London, 1969.

Rosen, S., "Electronic Computers, A Historical Survey," *Computing Surveys,* Vol. 1, No. 1 (March), 1969.

Sanders, D. H., *Computers in Business,* An Introduction, McGraw-Hill, New York, 1968.

Stark, P. A., *Digital Computer Programming,* MacMillan, New York, 1967.

Weiss, E. C., *Computer Usage Fundamentals,* McGraw-Hill, New York, 1969.

9

Sorting

1. Introduction

One of the operations most frequently performed in data processing consists of arranging data into sequential order according to some predetermined criteria. This process is called sorting. Data may be sorted either numerically or alphabetically. Consider, for example, a payroll file which contains a number of records, one for each employee. Each record contains an employee name and an employee number, in addition to other information. In numeric sorting we arrange the file in ascending (or descending) order according to the employee's number. In alphabetic sorting we arrange the file alphabetically using the employee's name. In either case, the item in the record which is used to sort the file is called the *key*. There are many ways of sorting records, the one usually chosen depending on the type of file and storage device used. In this chapter we shall consider card sorting, several types of internal sorting, and tape sorting.

2. Card Sorting

If the file to be sorted is stored on cards (one record per card), then the records can be sorted using a card sorter. A card sorter, which may read up to 1000 cards per minute, places each card in its proper physical position in the file. This operation is a very common one in data processing since most transaction files are stored on cards.

173

In order to explain the operation of a card sorter we must first give a simplified description of the device itself. A card sorter consists of a stacker into which the cards to be sorted are placed, a set of 13 pockets (or hoppers) into which the cards fall, and two switches. One switch is used to select either a sort on zone or digit punches, while the other specifies the column of the card to be used in the sorting process. The 13 pockets correspond to the 12 punch positions in any column of the card and a reject pocket if no holes are present. During digit sorts only pockets 0 to 9 are filled while a zone sort uses only pockets 12, 11, and 0.

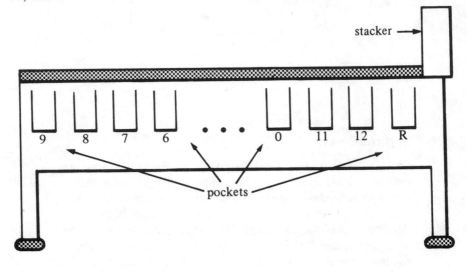

FIGURE 9a: A card sorter.

Assume that we wish to sort a set of cards, which contain a two digit number in columns 4 and 5, into ascending order. We set the column selector to column 5, the hole selector to digit and start the sorter. Each card is inspected and is placed in one of the pockets 0–9 depending on the digit punch found. Thus, after one pass the cards are sorted according to their last (or least significant) digit. The cards are now collected from the ten pockets, the contents of the 9's pocket being placed on top of those in the 8's pocket, which are placed on top of those in the 7's pocket, and so on. The cards are then placed back in the stacker, the column selector set to column 4 and the process repeated. If we stack the cards as before (that is, 9's on top of 8's, etc.) then we will have the set of cards in ascending order if we work from the bottom to the top of the stack.

It is probably not obvious that the procedure described above really sorts the cards into the proper order, so we illustrate the process in Figure 9b using a set of 2 digit numbers which we call **A**. Remember that we always work from the bottom of a stack to the top.

A	Pocket	Contents	A	Pocket	Contents	A
77			19			92
26	0	70	38	0	01	87
70	1	01, 21, 11	77	1	11, 19	77
54	2	92	87	2	21, 26, 26	70
64	3	43	26	3	36, 38	64
36	4	64, 54	36	4	43	55
55	5	55	26	5	54, 55	54
11	6	26, 36, 26	55	6	64	43
38	7	87, 77	54	7	70, 77	38
21	8	38	64	8	87	36
87	9	19	43	9	92	26
92			92			26
43	Results of		11	Results of		21
26	First pass		21	Second pass		19
01			01			11
19			70			01

original data (unsorted)	first collection (sorted by last digit)	second collection (completely sorted)

FIGURE 9b: An example of numeric card sorting.

We conclude this section with two remarks. First, if we sort a set of cards which contain a 5 digit number in columns 1 to 5, we use the same process described above but five passes through the card sorter are required. One each on columns 5, 4, 3, 2, and 1, in that order. Second, for alphabetic sorting we use the same technique of moving right to left on the card, but two passes are required on each column, one sorting by zone and the other sorting by digit.

Exercises

1. Using the procedure described in this section, sort the following set of numbers by hand.

$$\{12, 26, 14, 13, 47, 32, 14, 02, 17, 05, 02, 82, 63, 71, 19, 03\}.$$

Illustrate the result of each pass as in Figure 9b.

2. Attempt to sort the set of numbers in Exercise 1 by sorting on the

high order digit first and then the low order digit. Does this process work? Show the intermediate results in a form similar to Figure 9b.

3. If a card sorter can read 1000 cards per minute, but because of human card handling its effective speed is only 500 cards per minute, how long would it take to sort 10,000 cards if:

(a) a 10 digit numeric field is involved?

(b) a 10 digit alphabetic field is involved?

4. Sort the following set of names by their first two letters showing each step in a manner similar to that of Figure 9b.

Don, Jack, Ian, Bill, Nancy, Betty, Larry, Byron, Ted, Paul, Pat, Bob, Ann, Sam, Frank, Carl, Rose.

Use the Hollerith codes given in Figure 8c.

5. Unit record cards have a front and a back side. Key punches print only on the front side of a card. Write a set of two digit numbers on a set of cards and sort them using the method of a card sorter. Always place the cards face down in the "pockets." Verify that when you finish the sorting process the cards are in ascending order when they are facing you. How would you modify the sorting procedure so that they were in descending order when facing you?

3. Internal Sorting

If the file to be sorted is stored in the internal memory of the computer, then there are many techniques available for sorting it. The one chosen in practice will usually depend upon the type of file, the amount of storage available, and other characteristics of the computer being used. In this section we shall discuss five methods for sorting files using main memory. We will assume that the key on which we are sorting is numeric, although the techniques discussed apply equally well to alphabetic sorting on a computer, since all alphabetic characters are stored as numbers. Since each record may contain many items, usually only the keys, and a set of pointers indicating where the full record may be found, are manipulated. This increases the speed of the sorting process considerably, since very little data is moved until the end of the sort, and then it is moved only once instead of possibly many times.

Consider a typical payroll file as shown in Figure 9c. The key in this case is the employee number (I.D.). One way of storing this information is to represent employee numbers by subscripted variables, that is, to place them in an array. The names and other data can be placed in other arrays. Since we are assuming that all the data is stored in main memory we have a random access file, and if we wish to refer to the nth record we merely consider the nth element in each of the arrays. To sort the data in Figure 9c we start with the keys and pointers as shown on the left in Figure 9d. After completing the sort, the keys and pointers would appear as shown on the right in Figure 9d. Since the pointer after each key indicates the location of the data associated with that key the remainder of the data may be easily placed in its proper location in the file.

	I.D.	NAME	GROSS PAY	TAX	ETC.
Record 1	10884	J. HOLMES	4519.63	473.11	...
Record 2	9963	E. BOWLES	4728.86	366.28	...
Record 3	11007	T. SCOTT	4430.11	452.16	...
Record 4	8176	F. GREEN	3921.00	301.72	...
etc.					

FIGURE 9c: Typical payroll file.

n	key	pointer		n	key	pointer
1	10884	1		1	8176	4
2	9963	2		2	9963	2
3	11007	3		3	10884	1
4	8176	4		4	11007	3

before sort   after sort

FIGURE 9d: Sorting using a pointer.

In the sorting methods given below we assume that the keys are integers, and that they are stored in an array A of size N. We also assume that the keys are to be sorted into ascending order. For each sorting technique we pay special attention to the storage requirements of the keys, the number of passes that must be made through the file (keys), the number of comparisons required to complete the sort, and the number of data movements involved in doing the sort. This information will give us a basis for estimating the cost and hence the feasibility of using a particular method in a given situation. Note that we do not consider the size of the sorting program itself, since it is usually small compared with the space occupied by the data being manipulated.

(a) Selection

This is perhaps the most obvious method of sorting. The array A is searched for the smallest element. This is then placed in an array B and replaced in the array A by a large number. The array A is again searched for the smallest number and this is then placed as the second element in the array B. Its position in the array A is again replaced by a large number, and so on. The method is illustrated in Figure 9e, where A has 4 elements. The number of passes required to complete the sort is equal to N, the number of items in array A. If we begin each pass by assuming that the first element of A is the smallest, $(N - 1)$ comparisons are required to determine if we are correct or to find the smallest element. The total number of comparisons is then $N(N - 1)$. Clearly, a total of 2N locations are required to store the keys and since each piece of data is moved once N data movements are required.

A	B	A	B	A	B	A	B	A	B
9	0	9	3	9	3	1000	3	1000	3
3	0	1000	0	1000	5	1000	5	1000	5
12	0	12	0	12	0	12	9	1000	9
5	0	5	0	1000	0	1000	0	1000	12
start		end pass 1		end pass 2		end pass 3		end pass 4	

FIGURE 9e: Sorting by selection.

A flowchart for the selection method is given in Figure 9f. In the flowchart it is assumed that the numbers being sorted are all less than 1000. If this is not the case then a number larger than 1000 will need to be used in the step $a_m \leftarrow 1000$.

(b) Selection with interchange

This method is a modification of the method of selection. The smallest element in the array A is found and interchanged with the first element of A. Then the smallest element of A, excluding the first element, is found and interchanged with the second element of A. Next the smallest element of A, excluding the first two elements, is found and interchanged with the third element. This process continues until the array is sorted. An example of this sorting procedure is given in Figure 9g.

The number of passes required to sort the array is equal to $(N - 1)$. This should be obvious, since when the first $(N - 1)$ elements are in order the largest element will be in the last position and hence in order also. As with the selection method, on the first pass the number of comparisons is $(N - 1)$. The second pass, however, requires only $(N - 2)$ comparisons, the third pass $(N - 3)$ and so on until finally on the last pass the number of comparisons equals 1. Thus the total number of comparisons is given by:

$$(N - 1) + (N - 2) + \cdots + 2 + 1 = (1/2) N(N - 1).$$

This is just half the number of comparisons required in the selection method.

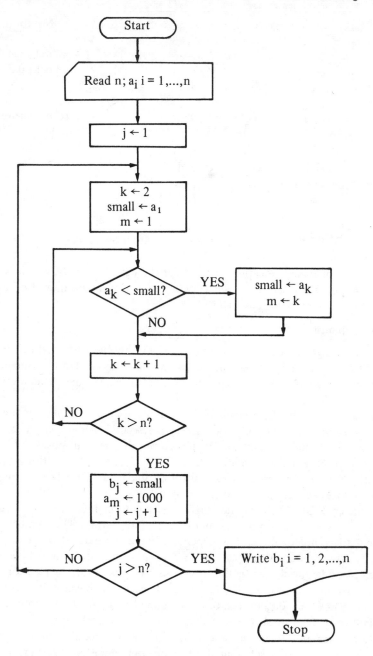

FIGURE 9f: Flowchart for sorting n numbers with values less than 1000 using the method of selection.

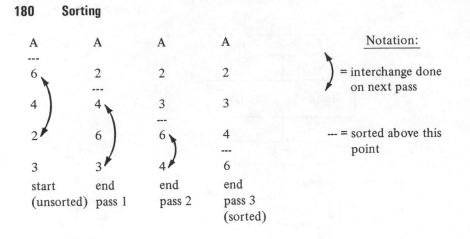

FIGURE 9g: Sorting using selection with interchange.

The number of storage locations needed for the keys is only N, which is also half of that required for selection. Since two pieces of data are moved on each pass, $2(N - 1)$ data movements are involved.

(c) Exchange

The exchange method is also known as the bubble sort method since items which are below their correct positions in the array A tend to move to their proper places much like bubbles in a glass of ginger ale. The method is as follows:

On each pass, the first element of A is compared with the second and the smaller assumes the first position. Then, the second element of A is compared with the third and the smaller is placed in the second position, and so on through the entire array. The array A is repeatedly processed in this manner until no exchanges take place in a pass through the data. The data is then sorted. Figure 9h gives an example of an exchange sort.

We see in Figure 9h how the smallest element (in this case 2) moves up one position on each pass until it is at the top of the array. The number of passes required to complete the sort is dependent upon the data. It is actually equal to $(L + 1)$ where L is the largest number of positions that an item is below its proper place in the array. In this case 2 is five places out of position and thus the sort requires six passes. The extra pass is necessary because in practice we do not know how far out of position the numbers are and the only way to be certain the numbers are sorted is to find a pass with no exchanges.

If the items are already in order, then the method requires only 1 pass. If the first item in the sorted set is in the last position, then N passes are required. It can be shown that, for random data, the expected number of passes is given by

$$\text{expected number of passes} = \frac{(1 + N) N! - \sum_{m=1}^{N} m^{N-m} m!}{N!} \qquad (9.1)$$

A	A	A	A	A	A	A ---
8	6	3	3	3	2	2
6	3	5	5	2	3	3
3	5	6	2	5	4 ---	4
5	8	2	6	4	5	5
11	2	7	4 ---	6 ---	6	6
2	7	4 ---	7	7	7	7
7	4 ---	8	8	8	8	8
4	11	11	11	11	11	11
start	end pass 1	end pass 2	end pass 3	end pass 4	end pass 5	end pass 6

--- sorted below this point

FIGURE 9h: Sorting by exchange.

It is not difficult to see that the value of equation (9.1) is less than N. Looking at Figure 9h we also observe that the sorted values settle out at the bottom of the array and thus $(N - 1)$ comparisons are required on the first pass, $(N - 2)$ on the second pass, and so on. These two facts taken together imply that the exchange method requires fewer comparisons on the average than either of the selection methods. On the other hand, it can also be shown that the expected number of data movements is $N(N - 1)/2$ which is larger than either of the selection methods when $N \geqslant 5$. The storage requirement for the method is N.

A flowchart for the exchange method is given in Figure 9i.

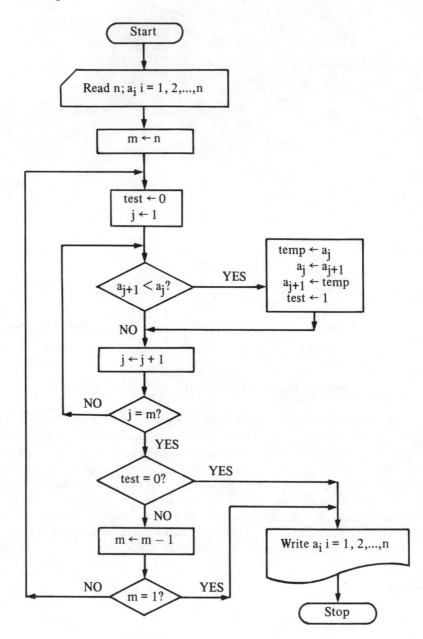

FIGURE 9i: A flowchart for sorting n numbers using the exchange method.

(d) Insertion

This method is similar to the way a person arranges his hand when playing cards. Items are taken one at a time and inserted into their correct positions. The method is illustrated in Figure 9j.

```
A
8    8    3    3    3    1    1    1    1
3         8    8    8    3    3    3    3
15            15   12    8    4    4    4
12                 15   12    8    5    5
1                       15   12    8    8
4                            15   12   11
5                                 15   12
11                                     15

start          partial sortings        end
(unsorted)                            (sorted)
```

FIGURE 9j: Sorting by intersection.

In order to implement this method efficiently a pointer to the bottom element in the set of sorted elements is required. There are two reasons for having this pointer. First, the bottom element must be the first element to be moved down if an item is inserted between two previously placed elements. Also, it must be possible to determine when the end of the currently sorted elements is reached so that the new item can be placed in the next lower location if it is larger than all the previously sorted elements.

For a set of N items a total of N passes are required. The number of comparisons depends on the data but on the average it would be $N(N-1)/4$. The number of data movements also depends on the data but would average $N(N-1)/4$. If the partially sorted elements are stored in A along with the still unsorted elements, which a little thought will show is possible, the memory required will again be N.

(e) Radix

The sorting method used on a card sorter and described previously in this chapter is an example of radix sorting. Quite clearly the technique described in Section 2 can be implemented on a computer. Using such a method has both advantages and disadvantages. The major advantage is that the number of passes through the data and hence the number of comparisons depends on the size of the key only and not on the number of items to be sorted. In particular, the card sorter requires $[\log_{10}K] + 1$ passes, where K is the maximum size of the key and [ ] means the largest integer that is less than or equal to the value of $\log_{10}K$. This value will probably be much smaller than N.

The major disadvantage is the storage space required. If we simulate on a computer the operation of a card sorter doing numeric sorting, then 11N storage locations are needed (10 pockets plus the stacker). This does not compare favorably with the other methods considered in this section.

Recalling that the number system used by most computers is binary rather than decimal, it might be more appropriate to perform a radix sort on a computer using only two pockets (0 and 1) and a stacker. In this case only 3N, and with a little thought only 2N, memory locations are needed. The sort then requires $[\log_2 K] + 1$ passes which may still be considerably smaller than N. Of course each pass requires N comparisons so we have $N([\log_2 K] + 1)$ comparisons in total. The radix sort requires a total of $2N([\log_2 K] + 1)$ data movements.

The five sorting techniques given in this section are only a small sample of the possible sorting methods which have been proposed for internal sorting. The reader who is interested in pursuing this topic further should consult the references at the end of this chapter.

Exercises

6. Write a program to sort a set of numbers into ascending order by the method of selection with interchange. Test your program by sorting a set of 25 random integers whose values are between 1 and 100.

7. Write a program for sorting by the exchange method. Test it by the method outlined in Exercise 6.

8. Write a program to evaluate Equation (9.1) for N = 1, 2, 3,...,25. Your program should also compute the expected number of comparisons for each value of N. Use this table to compare the exchange method with the other methods of this section if:

(a) comparisons and data movements have equal cost.

(b) comparisons cost twice as much as data movements.

(c) comparisons cost half as much as data movements.

9. Verify the correctness of Equation (9.1) for N = 2 and N = 3.

10. Write a program to perform a radix sort (base 2) and test it by sorting a set of 25 random integers.

11. Write a program for the method of insertion and test it as in Exercise 6.

12. Write a program which will read 10 records of the type shown in Figure 9a. Assuming that I.D. is the key, sort the input using only a key and pointer as discussed in the introduction to this section. Print both the unsorted and the sorted file.

13. Repeat Exercise 12 but assume that the key is the name (NAME). It

will be necessary for you to know exactly how alphabetic characters are represented in the computer you are using.

14. An obvious modification of the exchange method would do the exchanges working from the top to the bottom of the set of values being sorted on odd numbered passes and from the bottom to the top on even numbered passes. Write a program to implement this idea and test it on the following sets of data:

(a) $\{12, 3, 4, 7, 9, 2, 15\}$

(b) $\{3, 12, 1, 5, 7, 9, 8, 10, 17, 13\}$

(c) $\{6, 7, 8, 9, 3, 1, 14, 15, 2, 5, 4, 10, 12, 13, 11\}$

Does this always, sometimes, or never reduce the number of passes required when compared with the exchange method?

4. Sorting Using Tapes

It often happens in practice that the file to be sorted is too large to be stored in the internal memory of the computer. Thus a sorting technique which uses an auxiliary storage device such as magnetic tape, is needed. Since data can only be retrieved sequentially from magnetic tape, sorting methods which require random access to the data cannot be employed. Methods which require a large number of passes through the data are also poor because of the time required to rewind the tapes after each pass.

Tape sorting usually consists of two distinct phases. During the first phase, the original file is used to produce small sets of sorted data called strings. In the second phase, these strings of data are merged (combined) into fewer but longer strings. This process is continued until finally the original file in sorted form is produced.

In the discussion that follows, we assume that there are four tape drives available labelled 1, 2, 3, and 4, and that the file which we wish to sort is initially stored on the tape on drive 3.

We begin by reading a predetermined number of records from tape 3 into the main memory. Using one of the internal sorting methods of the previous section we sort these records and then write the sorted set onto tape 1. Having done this, we read a second set of records of the same size from tape 3, sort them, and place the resulting string on tape 2. We continue this process placing the sorted sets alternately on tapes 1 and 2 until all the file on tape 3 has been read, partially sorted, and written onto the tapes on drives 1 and 2.

If we assume that there are 1600 records in the file and that each internal sort puts 200 of these records in order, we have the situation illustrated in Figure 9k.

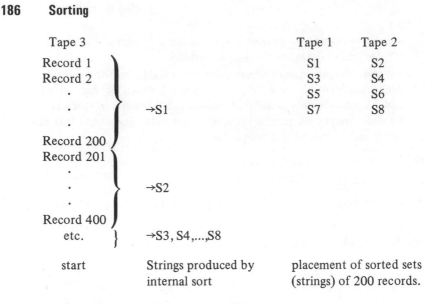

FIGURE 9k: First phase of tape sorting.

We are now ready to begin the merging of the two tapes. The procedure is as follows. Rewind tapes 1, 2, and 3. One record from S1 and one record from S2 are then read. The record with the smaller key is placed on tape 3 and a new record is read from whichever tape the smaller key came from. The current keys from tapes 1 and 2 are again compared and the record with the smaller key is written onto tape 3. This process is repeated until all the values from strings S1 and S2 have been written on tape 3 as a sorted set. We repeat the process with strings S3 and S4 placing the results this time on tape 4. The result of continuing this procedure are illustrated in Figure 9l.

Tape 1	Tape 2	Tape 3	Tape 4
S1	S2	S1-2	S3-4
S3	S4	S5-6	S7-8
S5	S6		
S7	S8		

tapes after internal sort   tapes after one merge

FIGURE 9l: Merging of two tapes.

Having again rewound the tapes, the roles of tapes 1 and 2 and tapes 3 and 4 are now reversed by letting tapes 3 and 4 provide the input which is merged alternately onto tapes 1 and 2. As can be seen in Figure 9m, if tapes 1 and 2 are then merged, we end with the sorted file on tape 3.

Tape 3	Tape 4		Tape 1	Tape 2		Tape 3	Tape 4
S1-2	S3-4		S1-4	S5-8		S1-8	not used
S5-6	S7-8						

tapes after 1 merge	tapes after 2 merges	tapes after 3 merges

FIGURE 9m: Completion of the merge sort.

From the above example it is clear that each merge reduces the number of sets by half, provided that at each merge there are an even number of strings to be merged. This will be the case if we start with 2^m strings where m is any positive integer. A total of m passes is required to complete the sort in this case.

A flowchart for merging two sets of sorted records is given in Figure 9n. It is assumed that each set contains L records, that the input is from tapes I and J and the output is on tape K (we are using the notation introduced in Chapter 8). We also assume that the records on tapes I and J have keys, KEYI and KEYJ, respectively.

As with internal sorting, a number of variations of the basic method given above are possible. For example, instead of performing a two tape merge, we may merge 3, 4, 5, or even more tapes on each pass. This clearly increases the speed of the sort since there are respectively only 1/3, 1/4, 1/5, etc. as many strings still to be merged on each succeeding pass. It may appear that twice as many tapes are needed as the order of the merge. This is not in fact true. It can be shown that a p-way merge can be done on (p+1) tapes using what is called a cascade sort. The interested reader can find a description of this method in several of the references at the end of this chapter.

Exercises

15. Illustrate the tape sorting procedure assuming a file contains 1600 records and it is possible to sort only 100 records internally. Use the same format as given in Figures 9k, 9l, and 9m.

16. Assume that tape 1 contains 5 sorted sets S1, S3, S5, S7, and S9 and tape 2 contains only 4 sorted sets S2, S4, S6, and S8. Illustrate how you would merge these 9 sets into a single sorted file. Use the format of Figures 9l and 9m. How many passes are required?

17. Repeat Exercise 16 but assume that tape 1 contains 4 sorted sets S1, S3, S5, and S7 and tape 2 contains only 3 sorted sets S2, S4, and S6.

18. Explain how you would sort a file containing 793 records if it is only possible to sort them internally into groups of 50 or less.

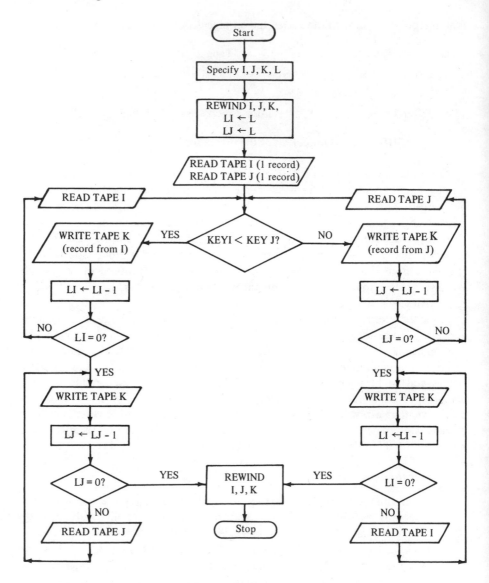

FIGURE 9n: A flowchart for merging two tapes.

19. Given a file with 2000 records and given that it is possible to sort internally up to 150 records, how many records would you sort internally in order to minimize the number of merges required, and also not do any unnecessary internal sorting?

20. Write a program which will load two strings of 10 records each onto two tapes and then merges them onto a single tape. Your output should show the two strings, as well as the completely sorted file.

5. Summary

The need to sort data is a very common one. The availability of computers has made it possible to sort very large files of data in a relatively short time. The software package supplied with a computer usually contains special programs which are designed to sort large files in the most efficient way possible on that particular machine. The method chosen depends on the type and speed of instructions available on that particular computer, as well as on the size of main memory, the availability of auxiliary storage devices, and the file and record size. A person doing a great deal of sorting should familiarize himself with the operation of such programs and use them, if at all possible, since they will save him time in the long run.

On the other hand, the person with only an occasional sorting problem in which relatively small amounts of data are involved will probably find it more efficient to write his own sorting procedure using one of the sorting methods discussed in this chapter. This is particularly true if all the data can be stored in main memory at one time.

Exercises

21. The method of selection with interchange although rather simple is a fairly good method to use as the first stage in a tape sort because the sorted string can be written on to a tape as the internal sort is taking place. This will reduce the time required to complete the sort because the tape writing time will overlap with the internal sort time. Can any of the other internal sorting methods given in this chapter be modified to provide this feature?

22. An interesting variation on the method of selection with interchange called the tournament sort proceeds as follows:

Divide the file to be sorted into two equal parts. Select the smallest element in each part. Compare these two elements and place the smaller in the first location of the array which will hold the sorted file. Select a new smallest element from the part of the file from which the smallest item came. Compare the two elements and again place the smaller in the array holding the sorted file. Continue the process until the data is sorted. The method is illustrated in Figure 9o. At each step the circled data is placed in the sorted list and a new smallest element must be found in what remains of that part of the file.

Start (unsorted file)	Smallest entry remaining in each part of file at each comparison						Done
3 7 2	2	②	③	7	⑦	empty	empty
4 9 1	①	4	4	④	9	⑨	empty
Comparison	1	2	3	4	5	6	

FIGURE 9o: An example of the tournament sort.

Write and test a program using this method.

23. Prove that the tournament sort requires about $n(n+2)/4$ comparisons to sort n records. How does this compare with the selection with interchange method for large values of n?

24. Does the tournament sort have the property considered in Exercise 19?

25. Generalize the idea of the tournament sort by dividing the file into 3 parts and show that to sort n records will require about $n(n+9)/6$ comparisons.

26. Assume we modify the exchange method so that it orders groups of three elements at a time. What is the maximum number of passes through the data if there are N elements?

27. Could the tape merging technique be adapted for use as an internal sorting method? Explain.

28. How would you decide how many records to sort internally as the first step in a 2-way merge? In a p-way merge?

29. How would you do a 2-way merge with only three tapes?

Further Reading

Brooks, F. P. and K. E. Iverson, *Automatic Data Processing,* John Wiley, New York, 1963.

Flores, I., *Computer Sorting,* Prentice-Hall, Englewood Cliffs, N. J., 1969.

Freiberger, W. F. and W. Prager, (eds.), *Applications of Digital Computers,* Ginn and Co., Boston, 1963.

Gear, C. W., *Computer Organization and Programming,* McGraw-Hill, New York, 1969.

Hull, T. E. and D. D. F. Day, *Computers and Problem Solving,* Addison-Wesley, (Canada) Ltd., Don Mills, Ontario, 1970.

Stark, P. A., *Digital Computer Programming,* MacMillan, New York, 1967.

Weiss, E. C., *Computer Usage Fundamentals,* McGraw-Hill, New York, 1969.

10

Information Retrieval

1. Introduction

The purpose of collecting data is to provide useful information to some group of users. In deciding how to organize the data, the most important question to ask the prospective users of the data is, "What do you want to do with the data once it is available?" In answer to this question we would get the following replies:

a. "I want to look at every piece of data."
b. "I want to be able to find and possibly alter any specified piece of data."
c. "I want to be able to add or remove any specified piece of data."
d. "I want to be able to find all data satisfying a certain property."

from

1. A payroll supervisor when considering a collection of employee records and making up pay checks.
2. The registrar when considering a collection of student records and change of course requests.
3. An employment supervisor when updating the records on currently employed workers.
4. A stock market analyst when requesting information on

193

the 10 most active stocks.

Looking at the types of information requests given above, we note that they can be characterized as being (a) sequential, (b) and (c) random, and (d) mixed. This chapter considers ways in which these various types of requests can be handled when the data is stored in a sequential linear list structure. (A description of this commonly used data structure is given in the next section.) In Chapter 11 we consider other data structures which are used and how they respond to requests for information.

In this chapter we use the word data in two ways. First, it is used to signify all of the information associated with the problem being considered, and thus is equivalent in meaning to the word file as introduced in Chapter 8. Second, the word data is used to mean an individual piece of information. In this case we are using the word to mean what record did in Chapter 8 or key did in Chapter 9. The context in which the word is used will make the meaning clear.

Throughout this chapter it is assumed that all the data can be stored in the main (core) memory of the computer at one time. For many problems this is not an unreasonable assumption since large, low cost, random access memory is available on most computers. It should be noted, however, that if all the data cannot be held in main memory then the type of auxiliary storage device on which the data must be stored significantly changes the analysis of the information retrieval methods given below.

Exercise

1. Give 3 examples of situations where the information required would be of type (a); type (b); type (c); type (d).

2. Sequential Linear Lists

Given a collection of data, D, one way of representing it is as a set of subscripted variables. That is,

$$D = \left\{ d_1, d_2, ..., d_i, ..., d_n \right\}$$

For the moment we do not worry about how the individual pieces of data are assigned their unique subscript but we do assume that some method is available for doing this. Also assume that the amount of storage space required for each d_i $(i = 1, 2, ..., n)$ is the same. Then, if the data is stored in memory so that the address of the first memory location containing part (possibly all) of d_{i+1} is one larger than the address of the memory location containing the last part (possibly all) of d_i $(i = 1, 2, ..., n-1)$ we say that D is stored as a sequential linear list.

It should be obvious that if the data is stored as described above and if the address of the first memory location containing part of d_1 is ADD, then the address of the first location containing part of d_i is given by

$$\text{address of } d_i = \text{ADD} + \text{LENGTH} \cdot (i - 1) \qquad (10.1)$$

where LENGTH is the number of storage locations occupied by each piece of data. Equation (10.1) says that if we know the subscript of the particular piece of data we are searching for, then we can find its location at once.

By way of contrast, if the data is not stored sequentially by the subscript assigned to each piece of data then Equation (10.1) is not valid and a more complex equation is required to produce the address of d_i.

Having defined what a sequential linear list is, we consider how well it is suited to answer each type of information request.

(a) Sequential requests

Sequential linear lists are ideally suited to situations where sequential requests are involved. As we move sequentially through the data, Equation (10.1) gives the address of the next piece of data very quickly.

The most common situation requiring sequential requests involves updating from a transaction file. As we noted in Chapter 8, this is done most efficiently if both the transaction file and the data in the list are sorted on some key. Thus d_1 might be the data with the smallest key and d_n the data with the largest key. The opposite could also be true, with d_1 having the largest key and d_n the smallest key.

We note, however, that the definition of a sequential linear list does not require that the data itself be sorted in the sense of Chapter 9 before subscripts are assigned.

(b) Random requests without additions or deletions

If the data is stored in a sequential linear list and there are random requests for information, there are a number of methods which may be employed in searching for the required data. We describe several of these methods.

The simplest approach is to use a *linear search*. The procedure is very simple. Look at the first entry in the list, if it is the required data the search is finished. If not, then the second, third, fourth,...,etc., entries in the list are looked at until the desired item is found or the end of the list is encountered.

We naturally would like to know how many comparisons, on the average, will such a procedure require. In order to determine this number, something must be known about the type of requests being processed. Assume that the requests for data are uniformly distributed over all the data available, that is, the probability of any particular piece of data being requested is the same as the probability of any other piece being requested. This means, of course, that if a large number of requests for data are processed, each piece of data will be requested approximately the same number of times.

Thus, we can determine what the average number of comparisons per data request will be, by assuming that in n requests for data each piece is requested just once. The n requests for data will then require a total of

$$1 + 2 + 3 + \cdots + n = \sum_{i=1}^{n} i = \frac{n(n+1)}{2}$$

comparisons. Since n requests are processed, on the average it takes

$$\frac{n(n+1)}{2n} = \frac{n+1}{2}$$

comparisons per data request. Clearly, if n is very large this is a large number.

In the next three sections we consider other ways of responding to random requests for information.

Exercises

2. Assume a telephone company stores the tariffs for long distance calls from a given exchange in a table of the form:

Area Code Dialed	Tariff
100	.50
101	.60
102	.55
. . .	
999	1.00

900 entries

If 20,000 long distance calls (uniformly distributed among all area codes) are made per day and each comparison costs .001¢, how much will it cost on the average to look up the tariff for any given call? How much would it cost per day, per month, per year to look up the tariffs for these calls? Could a programmer pay for his job by reducing the number of comparisons required? Do you think the assumption of a uniform distribution of long distance calls is reasonable? Explain.

3. Assume that a table contains 10 pieces of data $d_1, d_2, \ldots, d_{10}$, stored

as a sequential linear list. If the distribution of requests for information is as given below,

data	d_1	d_2	d_3	d_4	d_5	d_6	d_7	d_8	d_9	d_{10}
% of all requests	5	20	5	15	5	5	10	25	5	5

what is the average number of comparisons per request if a linear search is used to find the required information? Can you suggest a better way of storing the data? Justify your answer.

4. A library contains 300,000 books. Information about whether a particular book is in or out is stored in a sequential linear list in a computer. An individual may determine if a book is in or out by typing in the call number on a typewriter terminal connected to the computer. Is having the information sorted by call number a good way to store the data if a linear search is to be used? Explain. Can you suggest a better way? How would you implement it?

3. Binary Search

Clearly a linear search of a sequential list can be very costly and other methods which require fewer comparisons are needed. One such technique is the binary search. This search technique is easy to describe but is slightly harder to program than the linear search. The procedure is as follows.

Assume the data is sorted in ascending order. Look at the middle element of the list. If this is the required data the search is finished. If this is not the required data, then the desired information is in the top or bottom half of the list. The half chosen is determined by comparison with the middle data element. Looking at the middle element of whichever half is chosen, either the data is found or only half of the half (i.e. 1/4) of the original list still must be searched.

To illustrate the above procedure consider the following example.

Example 10–1. A small company produces 15 products. It keeps an inventory record for each product in the form

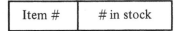

Item #	Inventory
007	33
020	456
023	
047	.
050	
096	.
107	
138	.
149	
210	.
211	
214	.
217	
314	.
315	538

Given the inventory table at the left, show the binary search pattern used to find how many of items #217, #214, and #096 there are in stock.

To show the search pattern it is only necessary to use the item #. The required search patterns are given below and on the following page.

Request for item #217

```
            007
             .
             .
             .
            107
middle → 138
            149                149
            210                210
            211                211
            214    middle → 214
            217                217              217        middle → 217
            314                314    middle → 314            &
            315                315                315        answer
```

Request for item #214

```
            007
             .
             .
             .
            107
middle → 138
            149                149
            210                210
            211                211
            214    middle → 214
            217       &        217
            314    answer      314
            315                315
```

(continued)

Request for item #096

	007		007	
	020		020	
	023		023	
	047	middle → 047		
	050		050	050
	096		096	middle → 096
	107		107	& 107
middle → 138				answer
	149			

.
.
.

315

FIGURE 10a: Examples of the binary search method.

In this example a maximum of 4 comparisons is needed to find any entry in the table. This is seen by observing that after 4 comparisons only $1/2^4 = 1/16$ of the table must still be searched. Since there are only 15 entries in the table every entry may be reached in 4 or less comparisons. This maximum of 4 comparisons per request compares favorably with the average of 8 comparisons required if a linear search is used.

Exercises

5. Assuming a uniform distribution of random requests, determine the average number of comparisons/request for the example given above if a binary search is used.

6. Does the efficiency of the binary search as compared with the linear search technique improve as we increase the number of elements in the table? Consider tables with 3, 7, 15, 31, and 63 elements when making your computations. Is there any pattern in the numbers given?

For a list with exactly $2^n - 1$ elements, where n is any positive integer, the binary search is easily implemented. We use the fact that at the k-th comparison we wish to look at the i-th entry in the table where

$$i = [(i - 1)\text{st entry looked at}] \pm 2^{n-k} \qquad (10.2)$$

The + or − sign is chosen depending upon whether the $(i - 1)$st entry looked at is above or below the desired data. Since the binary search starts by looking at the entry in position 2^{n-1} we see that at the k-th comparison

$$i = 2^{n-1} \pm 2^{n-2} \pm 2^{n-3} \pm \cdots \pm 2^{n-k}.$$

A flowchart for finding the required data R in a table with elements d_1, $d_2, \ldots, d_m$, where $m = 2^n - 1$, is given in Figure 10b.

Exercises

7. Write a program to perform a binary search on a table of 15 elements. Test the program by using a random number generator to produce the fifteen entries in the table. After sorting the resulting table search for each entry, by starting the random number generator over again. Output should give the table sorted in ascending order, followed by the values being searched for and the number of comparisons required to find them.

8. Explain how you would do a binary search on a list with 9 entries. Would your program of Exercise 7 work? Test it and see.

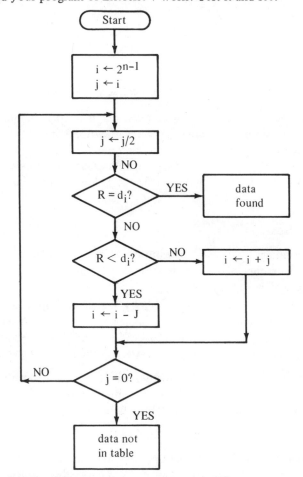

FIGURE 10b: Binary search when there are $2^n - 1$ elements in the list.

In cases like that of Exercise 8, where the number of entries does not equal $2^n - 1$ there are several ways to implement the binary search. First, extra elements could be added to the list. If the list has 29 elements adding two dummy elements would not cost much. But, if the list had 33 elements, adding 30 dummy elements would nearly double the storage cost. A second possibility is to change the algorithm given in Figure 10b.

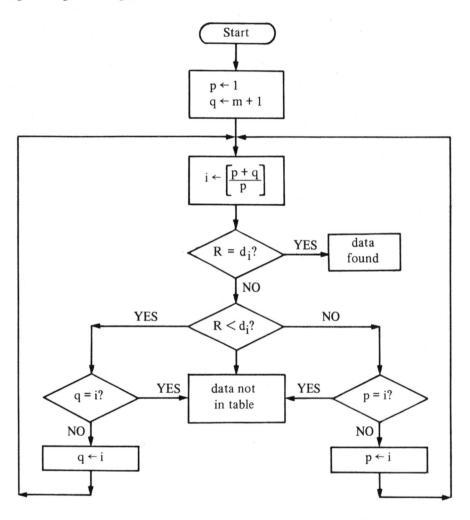

FIGURE 10c: Binary search of a list with m elements.

Exercises

9. Write a program to test the algorithm given in Figure 10c for the values m = 5, 6, 7, 8, 9. Let the list being searched be the integers 1 to m and search for all the integers in each list. Output should be similar to that in Exercise 7.

10. Show that if q is initially assigned the value m instead of (m + 1) in the flow chart in Figure 10c, then the whole list will not be searched.

4. Probabilistic Search

As an alternative to the binary search technique we consider a method similar to that which a person uses when searching for a word in a dictionary. The method used begins by opening the book to the most probably location of the word. Based on what is found, a search forwards or backwards may be necessary until the desired entry is found. The strategy used for searching forwards or backwards depends upon how close the required data appears to be. We refer to this technique as a probabilistic search because of the way the first guess is made.

A natural question to ask is how do we implement a probabilistic search on a computer and how well does it compare with other methods? The answer to the first part of the question is relatively easy. Assume we have a list with 200 entries and that each entry has a key with a value between 0 and 9999. If the values of the keys are uniformly distributed and if the list has been sorted into ascending order, then the most probable location (subscript) for an entry whose key has value K is

$$i = \frac{K \times 200}{10000} + 1 \tag{10.3}$$

If the data is not found in this most probable location, then we search (possibly using a linear search) above or below this point until the desired value is found.

Obviously the success of the probabilistic search depends on the data being searched. If the keys are uniformly distributed then the method words well. If the data is not uniformly distributed then the method does not work well without suitable modification to take into account the skewness of the distribution.

Exercises

11. Use a random number generator to produce a table of 50 integers in the range 0 to 9999. Use the same random number generator to search for 10 entries in the table both by a binary and a probabilistic search. Which method appears to be the most efficient based on the number of comparisons required?

12. Is it reasonable to assume that alphabetic data is uniformly distributed? Justify your answer. A telephone book, a dictionary, a library card catalogue, or simply the page from any book should give you enough information to answer this question.

13. How would you modify your probabilistic search algorithm if 60% of the values in a table of 100 values are uniformly distributed between 0 and 4999 and 40% of the values are uniformly distributed between

5000 and 9999?

14. Use a random number generator to produce 30 random integers between 0 and 4999 and 20 random integers between 5000 and 9999. Search for the first six integers produced in the range 0 to 4999 and the first 4 integers produced in the range 5000 to 9999 using

(a) a binary search based on Figure 10c.

(b) a probabilistic search based on Equation (10.3).

(c) a probabilistic search based on Exercise 13.

Which method gives the best results?

5. Hashing

Both the binary and probabilistic search methods require that the data being searched is sorted. Since sorting can be an expensive process a natural question might be, could we find efficient information retrieval techniques for data which is not sorted? The answer is a definite yes provided we have control over where that data is placed in the list initially.

Example 10–2. Consider the case of a school which has a two level grading system, i.e. it assigns letter grades for individual classes but converts these letter grades to a numeric value in order to compute a grade point average. Assuming that the grades range from A+ to F as shown in Figure 10d, and that the various letter grades have the machine representation also given in Figure 10d, we want to set up a table to get the numeric equivalent value given only the machine representation.

Letter Grade	Assumed machine representation of letter grade	Numeric Value
A+	2120	10
A	2160	9
A−	2180	8
B+	2220	7
B	2260	6
B−	2280	5
C+	2320	4
C	2360	3
C−	2380	2
D	2460	1
F	2660	0

FIGURE 10d: A school grading system.

Let the variable ALPHGR be assigned the value of the machine representation of any letter grade given in Figure 10d. Then it can be shown that the program given in Figure 10e will transform each machine representation of a letter grade into an integer, K, between 1 and 11, with no two machine representations producing the same integer.

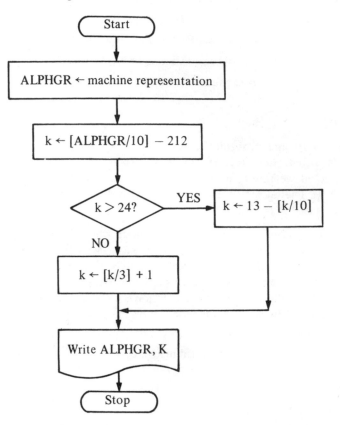

FIGURE 10e: A program for producing the integers from 1 to 11.

If the numeric values of the letter grades are stored in the proper order in a sequential linear list, then the value of K can be taken as the location subscript and the numeric value of the letter grade can be found immediately.

The program given in Figure 10e is an example of what is called a *hashing* function. It is characterized by the property that the data used in the search takes an active part in determining the address where we search for the data. In this particular case the address produced is the exact location of the required value.

Exercises

15. Verify that the program in Figure 10e transforms the machine representations given in Figure 10d into numbers between 1 and 11 and that there are no repetitions.

16. Using the results of Exercise 15 show that the numeric values of the letter grades should be stored as follows.

i	1	2	3	4	5	6	7	8
d_i	10	9	8	7	6	5	4	0

i	9	10	11
d_i	3	1	2

17. Assume that a grade of E with machine representation of 2560 and numeric equivalent of 0 is added to the grading system. Will the above hashing function still work? Explain.

The above example is somewhat special since the entries in the list could be expected to remain unchanged for long periods of time and the table (Figure 10d) was fairly small. Because of this an exact hashing function could be found, that is, one which always produced the correct location in the list on the first try.

Example 10–3. A small company employs 18 salesmen. The president of the company wishes to have a master file, containing the sales figures for each salesman, which he can interrogate at any time by typing in a salesman's name using a typewriter terminal located in his office.

Since salesmen tend to change jobs rather frequently, there is little point in even attempting to produce an exact hashing function since it would only need to be changed in a short time anyway. Instead, we attempt to find a function which will work for most cases and then develop a procedure to take care of the exceptions. Assume that when the system was set up that the salesmen were as given in the left hand column of Figure 10f.

Looking at the machine representation of the first three letters of their last names we see that there is going to be a problem since Grant and Graham have the same first three letters. Since this could happen no matter how many letters were chosen we will not add a 4th letter but treat this as we treat any other collision. (If an attempt is made to find two or more items in the same position in a list we say a collision has occurred.) We now need a hashing function which

Salesman	Assumed machine representation of first three letters in salesman's last name
Alan, A. C.	214321
Bedocs, L.	222524
Bennett, E. L.	222545
Evans, I. R.	256521
Finch, C.	263145
Grant, F. J.	275121
Graham, F. A.	275121
Harris, W.	302151
Henderson, H. E.	302545
Ing, A. K.	314527
Jones, T. P.	414645
Kolb, B. L.	424643
Martin, C.	442151
Meyer, R. T.	442570
Morris, R. M.	444651
Ryan, A. T.	517021
Steen, B. B.	626325
Winter, D.	663145

FIGURE 10f: Salesmen working for a small company.

will have as input the machine representation of the first three letters of the name and as output will produce an integer between 1 and 18. Assuming that the smallest value that the machine representation can be is 212121 (corresponding to Aaa) and the largest value it can be is 717171 (corresponding to Zzz) we consider three hashing functions.

Denoting the machine representation by MREP and the integers produced by the three hashing functions as IOHASH1, IOHASH2, and IOHASH3 respectively, they are:

(a) IOHASH1 = (MREP x 18)/717171 + 1,

(b) IOHASH2 = MOD(MREP, 18) +1,

(c) IOHASH3 = MOD(MOD((MREP x MREP)/1000, 100000), 18) +1.

Note: MOD(I_1, I_2) is used in the second and third examples given above to denote the modulus function whose value is the remainder when integer I_1 is divided by integer I_2. For example

$$MOD\ (12, 7) = 5$$
$$MOD\ (32, 5) = 2$$
$$MOD\ (214324, 15) = 4$$

We will assume that this function is available as a standard function although the reader may have to write a MOD function if it is not part of his particular language implementation.

The output from these three hashing functions is given in Figure 10g.

MREP	IOHASH1	IOHASH2	IOHASH3*
214321	6	14	12
222524	6	9	11
222545	6	12	16
256521	7	4	18
263145	7	4	4
275121	7	10	17
275121	7	10	17
302151	8	4	7
302545	8	2	16
314527	8	14	18
414645	11	16	3
424643	11	6	6
442151	12	18	1
442570	12	5	3
444651	12	16	4
517021	13	8	5
626325	16	16	8
663145	17	8	2

*The values given for (c) are the correct values of IOHASH3 if the product MREP x MREP can be stored exactly in the computer. Since this product is too large an integer to be represented exactly on some computers the output of this hashing function may be different when it is run on your computer.

FIGURE 10g: Output from various hashing functions.

The number of different integers between 1 and 18 is easily found and is given in Figure 10h. The number of collisions, that is, the number of times the hashing function gives repetitious values, is also given.

Method	a	b	c
distinct integers	8	11	13
number of collisions	10	7	5

FIGURE 10h: A comparison of hashing functions.

Since there is one inherent collision in the data as given, we see that the function given in (c) is quite good at giving different locations while the function given in (a) although simple is rather poor.

The superiority of function (c) can be explained as follows. In taking the product of MREP with itself we cause all the digits to interact with each other. In dividing by 1000 the least significant digits of the product, whose value represents the interaction of only a few of the digits of MREP, are discarded. By taking MOD(mw, 100000) the leading digits of the product which also reflect only the leading digits of the number being hashed are also discarded. The only digits which remain are the middle digits of the product and these have the greatest interaction of the original digits. Assuming the set of numbers produced by taking the middle digits of the product is uniformly random, then the remainders on division by 18 should be also. As Figure 10h shows the assumption does appear to be roughly satisfied.

Exercises

18. Method (a) does not take advantage of the fact that the smallest value of MREP is 212121. Modify (a) to take this into account and test the resulting hashing function.

19. Verify that the hashing function given by

$$\text{(d) IOHASH4} = \text{MOD}(\Sigma \text{ digits}, 18) + 1$$

is as good a hashing function as (c) where Σ digits is the sum of the individual digits in MREP.

20. How would you modify the hashing functions (a), (b), (c), and (d) if there were 100 salesmen?

21. Would you expect the hashing function (d) to be as good as (c) if there were 100 salesmen? Explain.

One problem remains and that is how are collisions handled? There are a number of ways this problem may be solved and we shall consider two of them.

One approach is to simply search the list sequentially, from the point where we had expected to find the entry, until it is located. A better approach is to have a pointer at the first location telling where to look next. This would require a more complex program. Exercise 26 suggests a third method.

Throughout the above discussion we have avoided the question of how to set the list of information up initially. Actually this is quite easily solved once we know what method we are going to use to retrieve the data. We use the same hashing function and conflict procedure to set up the list that we will use during the information retrieval stage. As with the other methods considered in this chapter, it is appropriate to ask how many comparisons on the average will be required to find a particular piece of information. Assume that the list can hold n pieces of data and that there are currently k pieces of data in the list. Defining the load factor α to be $\alpha = k/n$, it can be shown that for hashing followed by a linear search to handle collisions the average number of comparisons C_L is approximately

$$C_L = (1 - \alpha/2)/(1 - \alpha)$$

provided the list being searched is not too small. If a set of pointers are included to indicate where to look next then the average number of comparisons C_p is

$$C_p = (1 - \alpha/2).$$

The average number of comparisons for the two search methods are given below in Figure 10i for various load factors.

a	.9	.75	.5	.1
C_L	5.50	2.50	1.50	1.06
C_p	1.45	1.38	1.25	1.05

FIGURE 10i: Average number of comparisons using hashing, followed by linear or pointer search.

We conclude this section with Figures 10j and 10k. Figure 10j gives the sequential linear list which would be produced if we were to create a list for the problem in Example 10–3 by reading in the salesmen's names in alphabetical order and placing them in a list based on the value of IOHASH produced by method (c) as given in Figure 10g. If a collision occurs we search sequentially through the list, starting at the next location following the location where we attempted to place the item, until a vacant space is found. The new list item is placed in this vacant space. If we come to the end of the list before we find an empty space then we start at the beginning of the list and continue to search sequentially until an empty space is found.

Included in Figure 10j are the number of comparisons required to find each piece of data if we start with the location given by IOHASH.

List Position	Salesman	Number of Comparisons
1	Graham, F. A.	3
2	Henderson, H.E.	5
3	Ing, A. K.	4
4	Finch, C.	1
5	Jones, T. P.	3
6	Kolb, B. L.	1
7	Harris, W.	1
8	Martin, C.	8
9	Meyer, R. T.	7
10	Morris, R. M.	7
11	Bedocs, L.	1
12	Alan, A. C.	1
13	Ryan, A. T.	9
14	Steen, B. B.	7
15	Winter, D.	14
16	Bennett, E. L.	1
17	Grant, F. J.	1
18	Evans, I. R.	1

FIGURE 10j: List positions for salesmen using hasing function (c) and number of comparisons required to find the data.

Figure 10k gives the flowchart used to produce the table given in Figure 10j. We assume that each storage location in our computer can store three alphabetic characters and hence 5 locations, $name_j$ $(j = 1,...,5)$ are used to store each name when it is first read. Clearly MREP = $name_1$ in this case. The sequential linear list is stored in a set of locations called $table_{ij}$ $(i = 1,...,18; j = 1,...,4)$.

Exercises

22. What is the average number of comparisons per request in Figure 10j? If a binary search based on Figure 10c is used to search the sorted list given in Figure 10f what will the average number of comparisons per request be?

23. Write a program based on Figure 10k, which reads in the 18 salesmen's names given in Figure 10f and places them in a list. Why is the order in your list different from that given in Figure 10j?

24. What is the average number of comparisons per request if we use the hashing function when searching the list produced in Exercise 23? How does this compare with using a sorted list and a binary search?

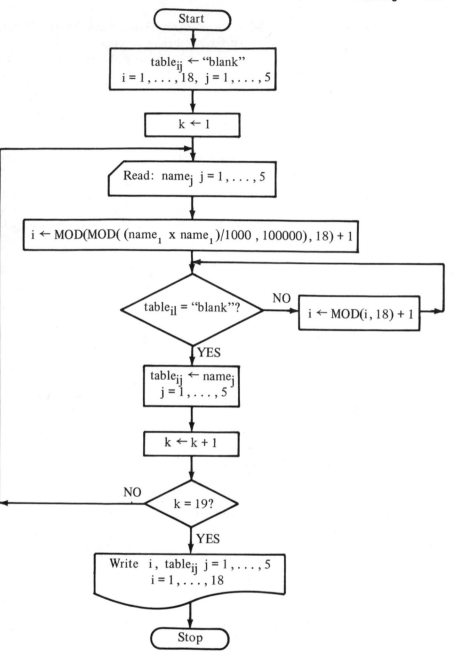

FIGURE 10k: A flowchart for producing a list of names using a hashing function.

25. In the list given in Figure 10j salesmen Winter, Ryan, Martin, Meyer, Steen and Morris required a large number of comparisons. No doubt a similar situation occurred in Exercise 23. Modify the program of Exercise 23 so that there are positions for

(a) 20

(b) 30

(c) 40

names. Does this reduce the number of conflicts and average number of comparisons per request?

26. Let K be the key we are searching for and let $H_0(K)$ be the first location produced by the hashing function. If $H_i(K)$ is the $(i + 1)$st location produced by our hashing function then the linear search used in producing Figure 10j can be described as

$$H_i(K) = MOD(H_0(K) + i, 18) + 1$$

Rewrite the program in Exercise 23 so that

$$H_i(K) = MOD(H_0(K) + r_i, 18) + 1 \qquad (10.4)$$

where the r_i are the following set of random integers.

i	1	2	3	4	5	6	7	8	9	10	11	12
r_i	6	0	7	14	9	3	1	8	15	2	5	4

i	13	14	15	16	17
r_i	10	12	13	11	16

Does this reduce the average number of comparisons?

27. A method based on Equation (10.4), where r_i is some random integer, is called random search method. It can be shown that the average number of comparisons C_r is given by

$$C_r = \frac{-1}{\alpha} \log_e (1 - \alpha).$$

Evaluate C_r for load factors of .9, .75, .5, and .1 and compare the results with those given in Figure 10i.

28. Repeat Exercise 25 using a random search method for placement of the data. Does it appear to require more or less comparisons per request

than the linear search method?

6. Other Types of Information Requests

Having considered in some detail how to respond to random requests where data is neither added or removed from the list once it has been created, it is natural to ask what happens if data is either added or removed.

(a) Random requests with additions and deletions

Under this heading we consider two situations

(a) the space occupied by the list must be kept as small as possible (no holes)

(b) the space occupied by the list must not exceed a given bound (holes permitted provided there are not too many of them)

Techniques for handling these two cases are easily developed.

For case (a) assume the list is sorted. It is then sufficient to keep a pointer which tells where the next available place is in the list. If an item is to be added a binary search is done to determine where it should go in the list. All records in the list below that point are then moved down one position starting at the bottom of the list and working up. The new entry is then added to the list.

To remove an element, a binary search is again done to find the item to be removed and then all records below that point are moved up one position.

The method described in the previous two paragraphs is a very expensive procedure, because of all the data movement, if the list is long or if the records in the list are long. To see this, assume that there are always about n elements in the list and that the additions and deletions are uniformly distributed over the list. Then to add or remove an item will require about $[\log_2 n]$ comparisons for the search and $(n-1)/2 \times$ LENGTH data movements, where LENGTH is the number of storage locations occupied by an individual piece of data. We leave further discussion of methods for handling case (a) to the Exercises and Chapter 11.

The situation described in (b) can be handled much more satisfactorily. We simply use a well designed hashing function to both place new data in the list and find the entries which are to be removed. We note that to remove data from the list only the key needs to be reset to a value which indicates the space is empty. If the cost of storage is not too high and the data does not need to be sorted the strategy in (b) will be far superior to that of (a).

Exercises

29. A used car dealer has a sales lot that will hold 20 cars. He wishes to have a sorted table which shows all the cars (by their license number)

which are on his lot at any time. Write a program which will keep track
of the cars on his lot using the data given below:

(a) Assuming a list with no holes.

(b) Assuming a list with holes.

Licenses of cars on lot at start	Cars in and out of lot in order of occurrence	
00103	in	40128
02514	out	30728
10852	in	20932
16029	in	12415
16058	out	10852
16073	in	60218
16092	out	16073
17302	in	18038
20832	in	14201
21283	out	84218
22451	out	20832
30728	out	40128
71329	out	00103
84218	in	16060
	out	16058
	in	18226
	in	15102
	out	16060
	out	12415
	in	66021

Compute the cost of running each program under the assumption that
each comparison costs 1 cent and each shift of data in the list costs 2
cents.

30. Another strategy which could be used if no holes are allowed in the
list and we do not require that the list be sorted would be to always put
new elements at the end of the list. To remove an element we would
then need to do a sequential search to find its location and then move
all remaining elements up one position. Write a program based on the
data in Exercise 29. Using the same cost figures employed in Exercise
29, which method is cheaper? Would you expect this to be true in
general? Explain.

(b) Random requests with multiple responses

In many situations the data being searched contains more than one record which will satisfy the data request. In such cases none of the searching techniques of the previous sections are entirely satisfactory. The main reason being that they were designed primarily to find individual pieces of data. If the file happens to be sorted on the property being searched for, a binary search could be used to get to the right part of the file quickly. Then a two directional linear search would be used to find all the entries on either side of that point with the required property.

If the data is not sorted on the proper key then the only way to be sure all the records from a sequential linear list have been found is to search the entire list sequentially.

In the next chapter we will introduce other data structures which will handle multiple responses more efficiently.

Exercises

31. Given the information in the following table, write a program which will be able to provide all records which match each of the following conditions.

    (a) License # = 1600XX (X = unknown)

    (b) Color = DBLU

    (c) Make = Ford

License #	Make	Type	Color	Owner
00103	FORD	2DR	LGRE	SMITH
02514	CHEV	4DR	DBLU	JONES
10852	PLYM	STWG	GREY	SMITH
16029	FORD	4DR	BRWN	JONES
16058	FORD	4DR	LBLU	JONES
16073	PLYM	CONV	BLAK	SMITH
16092	MGMG	CONV	DBLU	SMITH
17302	OPEL	2DR	DGRE	SMITH
20832	FORD	4DR	LRED	SMITH
21283	CHEV	STWG	LBLU	SMITH
22451	CHEV	4DR	PINK	SMITH
30728	PLYM	2DR	BLAK	SMITH
71329	FORD	2DR	LGRE	SMITH
84218	PLYM	4DR	DBLU	SMITH

Would it be reasonable to sort the list before answering each request? Why?

7. Summary

This chapter has considered how information may be stored and retrieved using a sequential linear list. This type of data structure, although very simple, can be used quite economically when processing sequential requests for information and on most types of random requests for information.

It is not possible to say that any one of the searching methods considered in this chapter is always best or always worst. This is because the speeds at which various types of instructions are executed differ depending on the computer being used, and because the cost of storage relative to the cost of executing a given sequence of instructions also varies. Even more important than the physical characteristics of the computer being used are the physical characteristics of the data. Most of the discussion in this chapter has been based on the assumption that information requests were uniformly distributed over the data. If this is not the case then clearly additional analysis beyond the level of this book is needed. A decision as to the technique to be employed in any large system should take into account both the data and the computer being used.

In the chapter which follows, other types of data structures are presented which are also well suited to handling requests for information. Before deciding how the data is to be organized, these structures should also be considered.

Exercises

32. Over its life time, is it reasonable to expect that a collection of data will only need to respond to one of the four types of requests given in the introduction? In answering this question consider:

   (a) Records for oil company credit card holders.
   (b) Student registration records.
   (c) Land registry records.

33. Devise an exact hashing function for the days of the week, that is, one which takes the machine representation of the first three letters of the day and produces a unique number between 1 and 7. Assume the machine representations of the days of the week are as given below.

Day	Assumed machine representation
SUNday	626445
MONday	444645
TUEsday	636425
WEDnesday	662524
THUrsday	633064
FRIday	265131
SATurday	622163

The location to which we hash will contain information about meetings, etc. to be held on that day.

34. Explain how a binary search could be used to make the method of sorting by insertion, given in Chapter 9, more efficient. Write and test a program which sorts by insertion using a binary search.

35. A highways department maintains information about the current status of 30 different sections of highway on a computer. A person may obtain the current highway conditions by dialing a specified number and when the computer answers dialing in the highway number of interest. Studies have shown that 10 of the highways each generate about 8% of all the requests and the remaining 20 highways each generate 1% of the requests.

Use a random number generator to produce 30 distinct integers in the range 1 to 999 and let the first ten integers produced represent the 10 most requested highways. Determine which of the methods discussed in this chapter (excluding an exact hashing function) will provide the given information at the lowest cost assuming that the cost in dollars for each request is computed by the equation

Cost = (average number of comparisons) x (number of locations
    used to store highway numbers) ÷ 3000   (10.5)

36. Repeat Exercise 35 but assume that one highway produces 20% of the requests, three others 10% each, six others 5% each, and the remainder 1% each.

37. Consider storing the highway numbers in Exercises 35 and 36 in two lists. If the highway requested is not in the first list searched then search the second list. Does this reduce the cost as computed by Equation (10.5)?

38. Give several examples where the requests for information would not be uniformly distributed over the data available.

39. Assume that an air traffic control computer receives updated infor-

mation about the direction, speed, and elevation of an airplane once a minute during the time the plane is traveling between airports but that this information comes every 5 seconds when the plane is within a radius of 20 miles of a major airport. How would you organize the list of planes in flight to take this into account assuming that on the average there are 300 planes in the air at any time and 40 of these are within one of the 20 mile circles? Is cost or speed the most important factor here?

Further Reading

Brooks, F. P. and K. E. Iverson, *Automatic Data Processing,* John Wiley, 1963.

Gear, C. W., *Computer Organization and Programming,* McGraw Hill, New York, 1969.

Knuth, D. E., *The Art of Computer Programming,* Vol. I, Fundamental Algorithms, Addison-Wesley, Reading, Massachusetts, 1968.

Meadow, C. T., *The Analysis of Information Systems,* John Wiley, New York, 1967.

Morris, R., "Scatter Storage Techniques," *Communications of the A.C.M.,* Vol. 11, No. 1, January 1968.

Williams, W. F. *Principles of Automatic Information Retrieval,* The Business Press, Elmhurst, Illinois, 1968.

11

Data
Structures

1. Introduction

A major item in the design of any large data processing system must be a study of how the data should be organized so as to allow the quickest and cheapest access to the information which it will be required to supply. In Chapter 10 we have already looked at one type of data structure, namely the sequential linear list.

In this chapter we compare the effectiveness of the linear structure of Chapter 10 with several other data structures.

The major emphasis will be on handling the last two types of requests, that is, random requests with additions and deletions, and multiple response situations. Emphasis is placed on these two cases because it is clear that sequential linear lists handle the first two types of requests quite satisfactorily.

2. Linked Linear Lists

The first type of data structure which we consider is the linked linear list. Unlike the sequential linear list the physical position of the elements in the list are not important. The list instead is held together by a set of pointers which are part of the elements of the list. To illustrate the features of linked linear lists, several examples are considered.

219

Example 11–1. Assume a 1000 bed hospital wishes to keep an alphabetized list of all its current patients. On the average 300 patients are released each day and 300 new patients are admitted. The problem we wish to solve is that of minimizing the number of data movements required to maintain the alphabetized list. Each time an admission or a release occurs it will be necessary to move, on the average, 500 patient records if the sequential linear list structure considered in Section 6 of Chapter 10 is used. This would mean a total of 300,000 data movements per day. Storing the records in a linked linear list will reduce this number and still maintain the list in alphabetized form.

To see this, consider Figure 11a. It shows a list with 10 patients. N gives the physical position of each patient's name in the list. The names are clearly not sorted alphabetically based on their physical position.

N	Name	Pointer	
1	Harris	9	
2	Bennett	8	
3	Morris	7	
4	Alan	2	FIRST = 4
5	Martin	3	
6	Grant	1	
7	Stone	*	
8	Evans	6	
9	Henderson	10	
10	Ing	5	

FIGURE 11a: A linked linear list.

Noting that the value of the variable FIRST is the position of the first name in the alphabetized list, we use the values contained in the column headed "Pointer" to specify which physical position to go to next. In this way it is possible to move through the entire list in the correct alphabetical order. The symbol * following patient Stone is used to denote the end of the list.

Assume that patient Evans is released. The list is changed to reflect the new situation by simply changing two pointers as shown in Figure 11b. Specifically the pointer in position 2 is changed so that it points to Grant instead of Evans because Grant followed Evans in the original list. Since none of the pointers point to position 8 it is no longer in the list starting with Alan and may be considered to be empty. Variable EMPTY points to the empty list which in this case is position 8.

Assume that Jones is now admitted. Position 8 may be used for this patient provided the pointers are again modified. The resulting list is shown in Figure

N	Name	Pointer
1	Harris	9
2	Bennett	6
3	Morris	7
4	Alan	2
5	Martin	3
6	Grant	1
7	Stone	*
8	Evans	*
9	Henderson	10
10	Ing	5

FIRST = 4

EMPTY = 8

FIGURE 11b: Two linked lists.

N	Name	Pointer
1	Harris	9
2	Bennett	6
3	Morris	7
4	Alan	2
5	Martin	3
6	Grant	1
7	Stone	*
8	Jones	5
9	Henderson	10
10	Ing	8

FIRST = 4

EMPTY = *

FIGURE 11c: Two linked lists.

11c. In this case the pointer after patient Ing is set to point to Jones and the pointer following Jones points to Martin.

Note that in removing an element from the above list no data was moved, only two pointers were changed. When a new patient was added two pointers were again changed and the data for one patient, that of the new patient, was moved into a position in the list. Thus the number of data movements has been reduced from 300,000 to 300 per day which is a significant improvement to say the least.

It should be clear that, using the above structure, it is now necessary to search the list sequentially starting at the position specified by FIRST when either adding or removing data. Thus the data structure replaces a large number of data movements with a large number of comparisons. Exercise 4 considers this problem in more detail.

Example 11−2. Consider the problem proposed in Exercise 30 of Chapter 10. It is clear that no matter how the data is sorted it will be necessary to search the entire list to satisfy two of the three types of requests. It would be natural to sort the list on whichever field of data requests were likely to be made most often. Linked linear lists provide a method for reducing the number of comparisons required for the other searches.

Assume that the information given in Exercise 30 is stored in an array with entries $MOTOR_{i,j}$. We assume that the i-th row of the array is assigned as follows:

$$
\begin{aligned}
\text{License \#} &= MOTOR_{i,1} \\
\text{Make} &= MOTOR_{i,2} \\
\text{Type} &= MOTOR_{i,4} \\
\text{Color} &= MOTOR_{i,5} \\
\text{Name} &= MOTOR_{i,7} \text{ to } MOTOR_{i,12}
\end{aligned}
$$

Note that $MOTOR_{i,3}$ and $MOTOR_{i,6}$ have not been assigned values. We use these two positions to store pointers which will connect similar types of data together.

$$MOTOR_{i,j}$$

i \ j	1	2	3	4	5	6	7	8
1	00103	FORD	4		LGRE	*		
2	02514	CHEV	10		DBLU	*		
3	10852	PLYM	6		GREY	*		
4		FORD	5		BRWN	*		
5		FORD	9		LBLU	*		
6	.	PLYM	12	.	BLAK	*	.	.
7	.	MGMG	*	.	DBLU	2	.	.
8	.	OPEL	*	.	DGRE	*	.	.
9		FORD	13		LRED	*		
10		CHEV	11		LBLU	5		
11		CHEV	*		PINK	*		
12		PLYM	14		BLAK	6		
13		FORD	*		LGRE	1		
14	84218	PLYM	*		DBLU	7		

FIGURE 11d: A set of motor vehicle records.

The easiest way to see the connections is to look at Figure 11d where some of the array MOTOR is reproduced.

Assume we wish to find all Plymouths. After a short search we discover that $MOTOR_{3,2}$ contains PLYM. Looking at $MOTOR_{3,3}$ we find the value 6. Checking $MOTOR_{6,2}$ we discover another PLYM. $MOTOR_{6,3}$ contains 12 and $MOTOR_{12,2}$ contains the next PLYM entry. After one more jump we find $MOTOR_{14,3}$ contains * indicating there are no more PLYM's in the list. Similarly, starting with the first appearance of any other make in the list it is possible

j i	MAKEPT$_{i,j}$	
	(key) 1	(first entry) 2
1	CHEV	2
2	FORD	1
3	MGMG	7
4	OPEL	8
5	PLYM	3

j i	COLORPT$_{i,j}$	
	(key) 1	(first entry) 2
1	BLAK	12
2	BRWN	4
3	DBLU	14
4	DGRE	8
5	GREY	3
6	LBLU	10
7	LGRE	13
8	LRED	9
9	PINK	11

FIGURE 11e: Pointer tables for motor vehicle registration.

to go directly to all others. The set of pointers for the color links follow the same pattern except that they work from the bottom up since that is actually how all the pointers would probably be ordered if the records are read into the table in ascending order by the license number. (See Exercise 5.)

The main shortcoming of the above structure is that it is still necessary to search a large portion of the list to find the first entry of the type we are trying to find. This problem can easily be solved by adding two short tables which we call MAKEPT and COLORPT. For the example under consideration MAKEPT has 5 entries and COLORPT has 9 entries. If the tables are as shown in Figure 11e then a binary search would quickly give the location of the first item of the type wanted.

Given a collection of data which is connected together with pointers, it is no longer possible to move the data around without regard to the other data in the collection. If we do, the connections which hold the data together will be completely destroyed. For example, if we place the record

07222	FORD	LRED	SMITH

where it belongs in the list in Figure 11d, then most of the records are pushed down one position resulting in the situation shown in Figure 11f.

$$\text{MOTOR}_{i,j}$$

	1	2	3	4	5	6	7
1	00103	FORD	4		LGRE	*	
2	02514	CHEV	10		DBLU	*	
3	07222	FORD			LRED		
4	10852	PLYM	6		GREY	*	
5		FORD	5		BRWN	*	
6		FORD	9		LBLU	*	
7		PLYM	12		BLAK	*	
8	.	MGMG	*	.	DBLU	2	.
9	.	OPEL	*	.	DGRE	*	.
10	.	FORD	13	.	LRED	*	.
11		CHEV	11		LBLU	5	
12		CHEV	*		PINK	*	
13		PLYM	14		BLAK	6	
14		FORD	*		LGRE	1	
15	84218	PLYM	*		DBLU	7	

FIGURE 11f: Motor vehicle registration with addition of a record.

It is easily seen that none of the pointers are correct any longer. This problem can be solved fairly easy by simply adding one to every pointer which is greater than or equal to 3. This same procedure must also be followed in the pointer tables.

Since a great deal of data movement and modification is required to place the new entry in the list at its proper position, it is better to have a third set of pointers which keep the license numbers in order no matter where they are stored physically in the list. Then the new record may be placed in position 15 of the table and still have the licenses in order. Figure 11g shows the modified MOTOR table with $MOTOR_{i,2}$ containing the license number pointer and all

$$MOTOR_{i,j}$$

i \ j	1	2	3	4	5	6	7
1	00103	2	FORD	4		LGRE	*
2	02514	15(3)	CHEV	10		DBLU	*
3	10852	4	PLYM	6		GREY	*
4		5	FORD	5		BRWN	*
5		6	FORD	9		LBLU	*
6		7	PLYM	12	·	BLAK	*
7	·	8	MGMG	*	·	DBLU	2
8	·	9	OPEL	*	·	DGRE	*
9	·	10	FORD	13		LRED	*(15)
10		11	CHEV	11		LBLU	5
11		12	CHEV	*		PINK	*
12		13	PLYM	14		BLAK	6
13		14	FORD	*(15)		LGRE	1
14	84218	*	PLYM	*		DBLU	7
15	07222	3	FORD	1(*)		LRED	9(*)

FIGURE 11g: Motor registration with license numbers kept in order using a linked linear list.

other items moved one place to the right in $MOTOR_{i,j}$. $MOTOR_{2,2}$ contains the original pointer value, in brackets, and the new pointer value after the new car has been put in the list. Note that $MOTOR_{15,2}$ contains the value that was formerly in $MOTOR_{2,2}$.

Thus far we have not considered how to handle the make and color characteristics of the new record. We look at that now. As far as the FORD list is concerned, every FORD is the same. For this reason, it makes little difference where the new entry is placed. Because we have a pointer table which points to where the first FORD in the list is located and we know where the new FORD is, it would seem most natural to place the new FORD on the front of the list. The same remark would hold for the color. Figure 11g shows the list constructed in this way. Note that the entries in the pointer tables given in Figure 11e must be changed also so that FORD and LRED both point to 15.

Another approach is to add the new entries on the bottom of their respective lists. In this case the pointer tables in Figure 11e would not change but the pointers in Figure 11g, in columns 4 and 7, would be those given in brackets. If new entries are added to the end of the list very often, it is obvious that a pointer to the end of the list should also be kept. Then it will not be necessary to search the entire list just to find the location of the last element.

To illustrate how the situation being modeled may suggest the list structure to be used we consider the following example.

Example 11−3. In a seacoast city, up to 200 longshoremen report to a hiring hall each morning. Men are assigned to work on ships and when they finish they report back to the hiring hall for a new assignment. It is necessary to design a system which will keep track of which men are available for work and which men are working.

There are several ways to do this. Two arrays $MENAVL_{i,j}$ and $MENWORK_{i,j}$ could be used to store the respective names. Assuming that it takes 10 memory locations to store each man's name this would require 200×10 memory locations to hold $MENAVL_{i,j}$ and the same number to hold $MENWORK_{i,j}$. A better approach, consistent with the discussion above, would be to have one array $MEN_{i,j}$ which occupies 200×11 memory locations and use the eleventh position in each record to store a pointer. This is the approach we shall use. Two pointers MANAVL, which points to the next man available to work, and MANWORK, which points to the most recent man entered on the list of men working are also required. Figure 11h shows the situation at 7:00 a.m. when the men report. Because space is limited we use only 10 men instead of 200 and give them names of A, B,...,J.

Assume that by 8:00 a.m. 7 longshoremen have been assigned jobs. Figure 11h shows the resulting table. Assume that at 9:00 a.m. longshoremen C, D, and F report back, in that order, for more work. Figure 11i illustrates one way the table might appear while Figure 11j illustrates another.

The situation in Figure 11i is an example of a last-in-first-out (LIFO) list, i.e. the last name entered on the list of men willing to work is the first one taken off the list. (The reader should check that this is what happens.) Such a list is often called a *push down stack* because of its similarity to the dish stacker found in many cafeterias and restaurants. If the longshoremen with the most seniority

j	$MEN_{i,j}$	
i	1-10	11
1	A	2
2	B	3
3	C	4
4	D	5
5	E	6
6	F	7
7	G	8
8	H	9
9	I	10
10	J	*

MANAVL = 1
MANWRK = *
7:00 a.m.

j	$MEN_{i,j}$	
i	1 - 10	11
1	A	*
2	B	1
3	C	2
4	D	3
5	E	4
6	F	5
7	G	6
8	H	9
9	I	10
10	J	*

MANAVL = 8
MANWRK = 7
8:00 a.m.

FIGURE 11h: Longshoremen assignment lists.

J	$MEN_{i,j}$	
i	1-10	11
1	A	*
2	B	1
3	C	8
4	D	3
5	E	2
6	F	4
7	G	5
8	H	9
9	I	10
10	J	*

MANAVL = 6
MANWRK = 7

FIGURE 11i: An example of a
push down stack.

	$MEN_{i,j}$	
i	1-10	11
1	A	*
2	B	1
3	C	4
4	D	6
5	E	2
6	F	*
7	G	5
8	H	9
9	I	10
10	J	3

MANAVL = 8
MANWRK = 7

FIGURE 11j: An example
of a queue.

are in general given job preference, then a push down stack is the obvious implementation to use. (Why?)

Figure 11j is an example of a first-in-first-out (FIFO) list. This is of course just another name for what is commonly called a queue. If the union is attempting to spread the work among all of its members then this approach would probably be used.

Exercises

1. Starting with the pointers as given in Figure 11c, show the new list after the following releases and admissions have occurred in the order given.

Martin	Released
Bennett	Released
Tolt	Admitted
Stone	Released
Franklin	Admitted
Adams	Admitted

2. Write a computer program which will start with the data in Figure 11c and will maintain a sorted list when the releases and admissions of Exercise 1 are processed. In order to verify that the program is working properly print out the complete list and the two pointers after each admission or release.

3. Explain why the linked linear list proposed for Example 11−1 would require 300,000 comparisons per day? If it costs .0001 cents for each comparison and .0002 cents for each data movement, how much money would the hospital save in a year by using a linked linear list instead of the sequential list structure of Chapter 10?

4. Assume a pointer table was included in Example 11−1 which gave the location of the first name in the list starting with A, with B, with C, ..., with X, with Y, with Z. How would this affect the number of comparisons done each day? Would it probably be worth storing these 26 pointers?

5. Write a program which will read in the records given in Figure 11d and produce the pointers and pointer tables given in Figures 11d and 11e. Is it easier to set up the pointers when working from the top or the bottom?

6. Modify the program in Exercise 5 so that cars may be added and removed from the file. Test your program by adding and deleting several records printing out the table in each case to be sure the pointers have

been set correctly.

7. In Example 11–3 a list of the men working is kept. Does this serve any useful purpose?

8. How many pointers are needed with a push down stack? How many pointers with a queue? Remember that efficiency is important.

9. Would a push down stack still work in Example 11–3 if the long-shoreman with the most seniority is always given the next job? How would you modify Figure 11i in this case?

10. Give two examples where a LIFO list could be used. Give two examples where a FIFO list could be used.

11. Many small desk calculators are now built with a push down stack memory. That is, there is a load button on the calculator and if a number is entered on the keyboard and the load button is pushed the number on the keyboard will be placed in the top of a push down stack. Thus the sequence

LOAD 3

LOAD 2

LOAD 4

produces the push down stack pictured at the right. These same calculators have buttons for +, −, x, ÷ where the effect of pushing one of them is (top − 1) ←
(top) $\bigotimes$ (top − 1) and old (top) is lost

4	(top)
2	(top−1)
3	(top−2) = bottom

($\bigotimes$ represents the button pushed). For example, ADD would modify the above stack to

6	(top)
3	(top − 1) = bottom

If this was followed by DIV, the stack would become $\boxed{2}$. Finally, there is a display button which permits the user to see the current contents of the top element of the stack.

Write a program to simulate such a calculator and test it using the following two sets of computations:

LOAD 6	LOAD 3
LOAD 5	LOAD 7
ADD	LOAD 5
LOAD 3	SUB

(continued)

MULT	DISP
DISP	DIV
END	DISP
	LOAD 3
	MULT
	DISP
	END

To save on data cards you may wish to punch more than one operation per data card.

12. A 1000 room hotel wishes to set up a complete information system for handling room reservations. Describe how you might design such a system taking into account the number of beds required, the cost of the room (a room next to the elevator will be cheaper than one overlooking the park), and current room occupancy. Assume a room can only be rerented when it is empty and has been cleaned.

3. Other List Structures

Thus far we have considered only one type of linked list, namely the singly

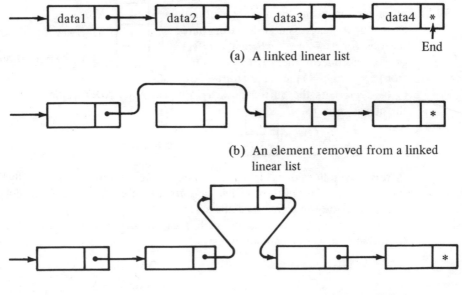

(a) A linked linear list

(b) An element removed from a linked linear list

(c) An element added to a linked linear list.

FIGURE 11k: Linked linear lists.

linked list which is pictured schematically at the top of Figure 11k.

Deleting data (b) or adding data (c) is quite simple since all that must be done is change pointers.

As noted previously, the list element which is shown removed from the list in (b) would not be left to "float around" but would be placed on some other list, possibly an available space list, just as the list element which was added in (c) came from some list.

Another possible structure is given in Figure 11l: This is quite naturally called a *circular list* since the tail of the list points back to the head.

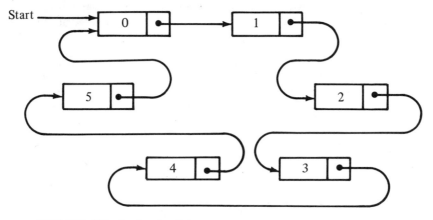

FIGURE 11I: A circular list.

Still another possible structure is given in Figure 11m. It is called a *doubly linked list*. Such a structure is useful for moving both forwards and backwards through the list.

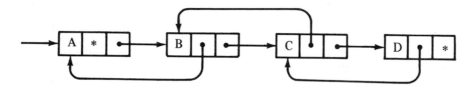

FIGURE 11m: A doubly linked list.

Exercises

13. Explain how the circular list in Figure 11l could be used to produce the value of MOD(I + J,6).

14. A computer accepts input from 25 typewriter terminals. How can we guarantee that all terminals will be serviced by the computer at

regular intervals?

15. Design a circular list structure to be used in simulating the movements of salesman who spends 3 days in town A, 5 days in B, 1 day in C, 3 days in D, 4 days in E and 6 days in F before starting over at A again. Weekends are not included in the above counts and must be added to the length of his stay if they fall during or at the end of his stay in a town. How would you include holidays in your program?

16. An airline in attempting to evaluate possible new routes collects data of the type given below for a set of cities A, B, C,...,L, M, N. How might they design simulation programs to test various routes for their aircraft assuming that they must return at regular intervals to a home base for service?

	(A & B)	(A & C)	(A & D)	(A & E) ...	(B & C)	(B & D) ...	(C & D) ...
0	0	0	0				
1	0	.05	0				
2	.1	.05	0				
3	.1	.05	.2				
4	.2	.2	.3				
5	.2	.2	.3				
6	.2	.2	.1				
7	.1	.05	.1				
8	.1	.05	.0				
9	0	.05	0				
10	0	0	0				

Probability of a given number of people wishing to travel between two given cities in any given hour.

17. A toy company wishes to test the design of a new game called "Cat and Mouse." The proposed game board design is shown below. The moves of the cat and the mouse are determined by a spinner which has equal probability of landing on any number between 1 and 4. Assume that the mouse moves first and that the cat catches the mouse only if he lands on the same square as the mouse or the mouse on the same square as the cat. Test the above game design by writing a program and playing 50 games to see if the cat and mouse each win about the same number of times. A game ends in a draw after 50 spins if there has not been a winner.

(See page 233 for game board design.)

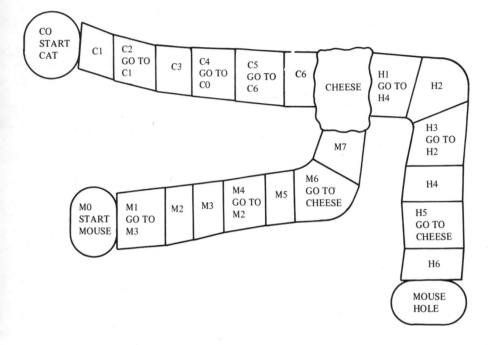

4. List Processing

We have now looked at a number of list structures. It should be apparent to the reader that they all have several common properties. First, we must be able to define a list element. Then it must be possible to use that element to start a new list or to add it to an already existing list. Finally, it must also be possible to remove an element from a list when it is no longer needed and place the area it occupied back in available storage for some other list element to use if needed.

Because lists and list processing have been recognized as important, a number of special purpose languages have been designed specifically with list structures in mind. LISP, IPL–V, and SLIP are examples of programming languages of this type.

List processing can, however, be done using many programming languages. The resulting program may not be as efficient as a program written in one of the specially designed languages mentioned above but for the person with only an occasional list processing program, the effort required to learn one of these languages may be greater than that required to write the program in the language with which he is already familiar. In any particular situation, an analysis of the programming costs and running costs over the life of the program will determine which is the better choice.

Exercises

18. Write a program using linked linear lists to handle the used car dealer problem in Exercise 28 of Chapter 10. Start with empty spaces for 20 cars and use

$$*\text{ADD} \quad \text{and} \quad *\text{REMOVE}$$

control cards to handle additions and deletions from the car lot.

19. The expression n! (Factorial (n)) can be defined in two rather different but equivalent ways. In the first, it is defined as

$$n! = ((\cdots((1\cdot2)\cdot3)\cdots)n).$$

This computation is easily programmed on a computer using a loop. The second method of defining n! is to say that Factorial (n) = n·Factorial(n − 1) if n ≠ 1 and Factorial (1) = 1. Thus

$$
\begin{aligned}
\text{Factorial}(4) \quad &= 4\cdot\text{Factorial}(3)\\
&= 4\cdot(3\cdot\text{Factorial}(2))\\
&= 4\cdot(3\cdot(2\cdot\text{Factorial}(1)))\\
&= 4\cdot(3\cdot(2\cdot(1)))\\
&= 4\cdot(3\cdot(2))\\
&= 4\cdot(6)\\
&= 24
\end{aligned}
$$

Write a program which will compute Factorial(n) for any value of n between 1 and 8 using the second method. Store the set of integers produced in expanding Factorial(n) (i.e. n, n−1, n−2,...,2, 1) in a linked linear list and then work back through the list to compute the final answer.

20. The polynomials

$$5x^3 + 3x^2 - 7x + 13$$

and

$$2x^3 + 2x - 4$$

are stored in two linked linear lists P1 and P2 as shown on page 235.

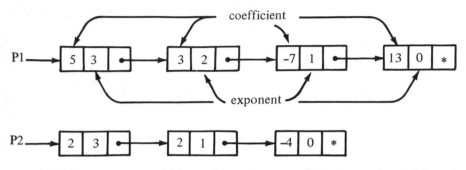

Write a program which produces the sum of the two polynomials and stores it in a list P3. Test your program on several sets of polynomials.

5. Trees

Once the idea that each piece of data may have more than one pointer associated with it is introduced, other interesting forms of data structure result. Figure 11n suggests one such structure.

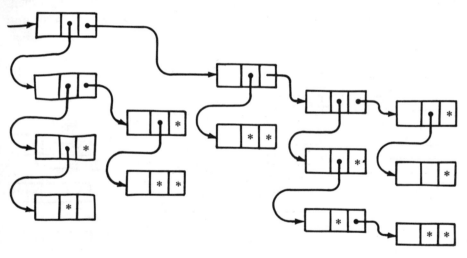

FIGURE 11n: A tree structure.

The structure in Figure 11n is called a *tree*. To see that this name is appropriate let the boxes shrink to points and connect them with straight lines. Doing this produces the structure given in Figure 11o which does look like a tree which is growing upside down.

The points where the tree branches are called nodes. Tree structures occur quite naturally in a number of applications areas. Several examples to illustrate their usefulness will be given.

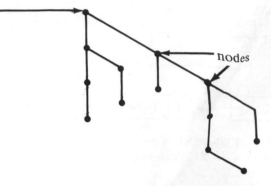

FIGURE 11o: A tree.

Example 11–4. We begin by considering the longshoremen problem given in Example 11–3 again. In our first discussion of this problem we assumed that men were individually assigned to jobs. Actually a group of men will be assigned to work on a given ship and will all finish and be ready for a new job assignment at the same time. A data structure of the type shown in Figure 11p is then suggested.

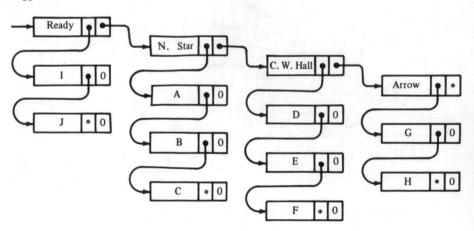

FIGURE 11p: A tree structure for the longshoremen problem.

In Figure 11p we assume that 3 ships, the North Star, the C. W. Hall, and the Arrow, are in port. The men working on each of these ships are listed below the name of the ship. A list of those men ready to work is kept under the heading labelled Ready. Note that the second pointer position for each man is zero. This labelled Ready. Note that the second pointer position for each man is zero. This pointer position is not needed in this particular tree structure since each man points to only one other man. We shall use this space to record how many days a man has worked. This will make it possible to compute each man's pay at convenient intervals. All values set equal to zero indicates that their pay has just been computed.

Assume that the C. W. Hall finishes loading and leaves port after 2 days. The tree structure will look like that of Figure 11q, assuming the work is spread around among the men available to work. As the figure indicates, only a couple of pointers need to be changed and the days worked recorded.

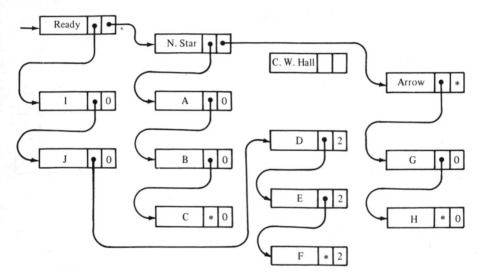

FIGURE 11q: The tree after C. W. Hall leaves port.

If a new ship, the Badger, enters port and needs 4 men, then the structure given in Figure 11r results. Although the data is shown in different positions from that of Figure 11q only pointers have really been changed. We leave for the reader to verify that if ships enter and leave port as given in Figure 11s then the resulting tree structure will be as given in Figure 11t.

Example 11–5. As a second example of a situation in which a tree structure would be appropriate consider the information about a group of houses which are for sale as given in Figure 11u.

When a person is looking for a house, he quite naturally has certain needs and preferences. Thus one person might want a three bedroom home with 2 baths while another wants a 2 bedroom home with 1 bath. If the data in Figure 11u is

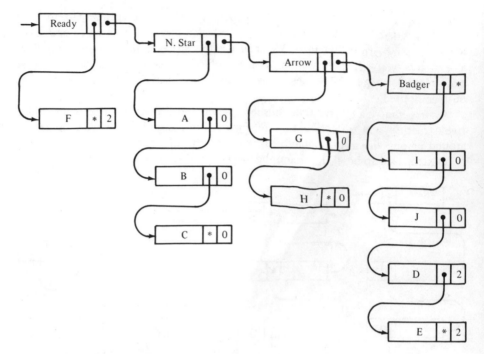

FIGURE 11r: The tree after Badger arrives in port.

Ship	Activity	Number of Men Assigned	Number of Days in Port
N. Star	Left	–	3
Willow	Arrived	2	–
Badger	Left	–	5
Hornby	Arrived	3	–
T. T. Next	Arrived	2	–
Hornby	Left	–	2

FIGURE 11s: Port Activity.

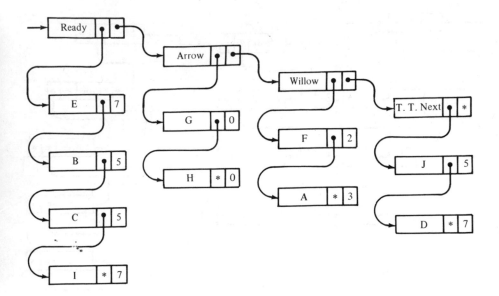

FIGURE 11t: Tree structure resulting from port activity.

House	No. of bedrooms	No. of bathrooms
A	4	1
B	2	1
C	3	2
D	2	1
E	3	1
F	4	2
G	3	1
H	2	1
I	4	1
J	3	2
K	4	1

FIGURE 11u: Houses for sale.

stored as a tree of the form shown in Figure 11v, then it is easy to get the lists of homes satisfying these typical requests.

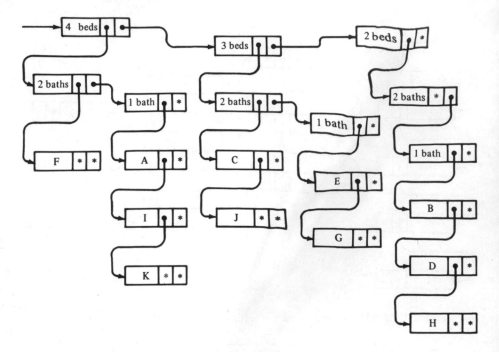

FIGURE 11v: Tree structure of houses for sale.

Example 11−6. As a final example, consider the design of an airlines reservation system. To be specific, assume there are 4 flights each day and that reservations can be made up to 4 weeks in advance. Figure 11w shows one way the data might be organized. Because of space limitations only a portion of the total tree structure is shown.

In the above examples we have considered only one type of tree, namely the binary tree. It is called a binary tree because at each node it is possible to go in only one of two directions. Quite clearly there is no reason why we could not have more choices at any node. All that is required is the availability of additional pointers at each node. Although changing the tree structure, this does not add anything new to the theory.

A second possibility would be to allow some of the branches of the tree to "grow" back together. This type of structure is called a directed graph. Although we give only a brief mention of directed graphs here, it should be noted that they constitute an area of current research.

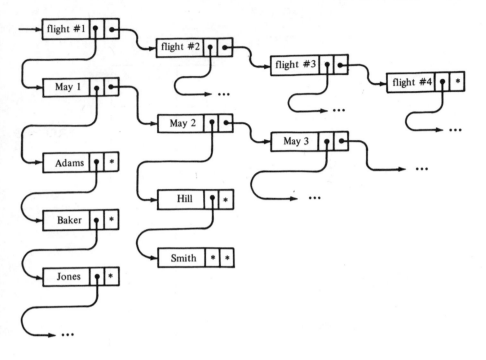

FIGURE 11w: A tree structure for airline reservations.

Exercises

21. Draw the tree structures which would result after each ship departure or arrival as given in Figure 11s and thus verify the correctness of the tree structure given in Figure 11t.

22. Assume the tree shown in Figure 11p is stored in an array $ITREE_{i,j}$ as pictured below. Write a program which will find and remove C.W.HALL from the tree. The tree should have the structure shown in Figure 11q after C.W.HALL has been removed. The space occupied by C.W.HALL should be placed on the free space list which currently starts at 15.

(See page 242 for array.)

$$ITREE_{i,j}$$

i \ j	1, 2	3	4
1	READY	10	12
2	A	3	0
3	B	4	0
4	C	*	0
5	D	6	0
6	E	7	0
7	F	*	0
8	G	9	0
9	H	*	0
10	I	11	0
11	J	*	0
12	N. STAR	2	13
13	C. W. HALL	5	14
14	ARROW	8	*
15		0	16
16		0	*

FREE = 15

23. Modify the program in Exercise 22 to handle all the port activity given in Figure 11s. At the conclusion of all port activity $ITREE_{ij}$ will have the form given on page 243.

$$\text{ITREE}_{i,j}$$

i \ j	1, 2	3	4
1	READY	6	14
2	A	*	3
3	B	4	5
4	C	10	5
5	D	*	7
6	E	3	7
7	F	2	2
8	G	9	0
9	H	*	0
10	I	*	7
11	J	5	5
12	WILLOW	7	15
13	HORNBY	3	16
14	ARROW	8	12
15	T. T. NEXT	11	*
16		0	*

FREE = 13

24. Consider the hotel room assignment problem given in Exercise 12. Describe how a tree structure could be used in this situation.

25. What type of tree structure would you use in Exercise 24 if advance room reservations were allowed?

26. A 1000 bed hospital wishes to design an information retrieval system to assist its doctors in seeing their patients. Specifically they want to be able to type in a doctor's name when he checks into the hospital and receive a listing of all his patients and details about their present conditions. Explain how the data in such a system might be organized.

27. The E. L. H. & E. railroad maintains records of all rolling stock on its tracks. In particular it must attempt to return all freight cars which it does not own to their proper owners. Assuming that there are only three types of freight cars, namely, box cars, flat cars, and tank cars and that railroad A is north, railroad B is east, railroad C south, and railroad D west, how would you organize the data given in the following type of input. (See page 244.)

car status	type	destination or current location	actual (or preferred) owner
Empty	box	Yard	A
Empty	flat	Yard	B
Empty	tank	Yard	D
Needed	flat	N	(A)
Needed	box	W	(D)
Empty	flat	Yard	E. L. H. & E.

You may assume that as soon as a freight car has been assigned to fill a need it is no longer part of the data structure you must consider. What will you do if there are no flat cars belonging to A in the switching yard and one is needed to go north?

6. Applications from Computer Science

One of the major application areas of the ideas contained in this and the previous chapter is the field of Computer Science itself. Several examples will be given to illustrate where this happens.

Example 11–7. Consider the problem of translating a program from a high level language such as FORTRAN, PL/1, or BASIC into the machine language which the computer understands. Each time a new variable is introduced in the program a storage location must be assigned to hold the value of that variable. Thus, as the program is translated, a table (called the symbol table) is produced which contains the name of the variable and the location where the value of that variable is stored. Other characteristics of the variable, integer or real and single or double precision, for example, are also included in this table.

As statements in the program are translated, each occurrence of a variable name means a search of the symbol table is required to determine what address is to be used in the machine language instruction. Usually a hashing function will be used to construct the table and to search it.

Example 11–8. A second problem in translating a high level language into machine language is converting assignment statements into proper machine code. Consider the assignment statement

$$y \leftarrow 1 + t \cdot (3 \cdot t + 2)$$

Because we can look at the entire right hand side of the assignment statement it is obvious which computations are to be carried out first. A computer, unfortunately, can look at only one character or symbol at a time and thus has no way to tell at a glance which operation to do first.

The problem can be solved in several ways. One of them is to employ a push down stack to produce sequences of operations similar to that considered in Exercise 11 of this Chapter. The procedure is as follows:

(a) We scan the assignment statement from right to left one symbol at a time.

(b) A right bracket ")" is always put into the push down stack.

(c) A variable or constant produces a "LOAD" instruction with the variable or constant as operand.

(d) An operator (+, −, ×, ÷) is placed in the push down stack if its priority is greater than or equal to the priority of the top entry in the push down stack. If the priority of the top element in the stack is greater than the current operator (except for right bracket) operators are taken from the stack until the less than or equal condition is satisfied. An instruction (ADD, SUB, MULT, DIV) is produced corresponding to each operator removed from the stack.

(e) A left bracket "(" empties the push down stack down to the first right bracket producing instructions corresponding to the operators removed.

(f) Finding the assignment operator "←" empties the push down stack and produces a "STORE" instruction with the variable to the left of operator as its operand.

The priorities assigned to the various operators are given in Figure 11x.

operator	priority
)	0
+	1
−	1
×	2
÷	2

FIGURE 11x: Priorities for operators.

We illustrate the process by translating the assignment statement given above into machine code. Each step of the operation is shown in Figure 11y.

246   **Data Structures**

Step	Symbol looked at	Operations performed
1	)	")" placed in stack
2	2	instruction "LOAD 2" produced
3	+	"+" placed in stack
4	t	instruction "LOAD t" produced
5	·	"·" placed in stack
6	3	instruction "LOAD 3" produced
7	(	"·" and "+" are removed from stack and "MULT" and "ADD" instructions are produced.
8	·	"·" placed in stack
9	t	instruction "LOAD t" produced
10	+	"·" removed from stack and "MULT" instruction produced. Then "+" put in stack.
11	1	instruction "LOAD 1" produced
12	←	"+" removed from stack and "ADD" instruction produced. Then "STORE y" instruction produced.

FIGURE 11y: Translation of the assignment statement y←1 + t·(3·t + 2) into "machine language."

Exercises

28. Assume that the typical student program has twenty variables and that on the average each variable is referred to 10 times in a program. If the symbol table has space for forty variables how many comparisons on the average would be required using:

   (a) a sequential search.

   (b) a binary search.

   (c) a hashing function.

29. Verify that the coding produced in Figure 11y, namely

> LOAD 2
> LOAD t
> LOAD 3
> MULT
> ADD
> LOAD t
> MULT
> LOAD 1
> ADD
> STORE y

correctly evaluates the given assignment statement.

30. Translate each of the following assignment statements into the machine language of this section using the six steps outlined in Example 11–8.

(a) $y \leftarrow t + (2 - (t{-}a) \cdot 6) \div 3$

(b) $y \leftarrow (((a + b) \cdot c + d) \cdot e - f)$

(c) $y \leftarrow ((a + b) + (c + d) \div e) \cdot f) - g$

31. Let $y \leftarrow x \uparrow 2 + 6$ mean $y \leftarrow x^2 + 6$, i.e. the symbol "$\uparrow$" is used to indicate raising to a power. What priority would you give "$\uparrow$" so that an assignment statement containing it would translate properly? Test your priority choice on each of the following

(a) $y \leftarrow x \uparrow 3 + 3 \cdot x \uparrow 2 - 2 \cdot x$

(b) $y \leftarrow (x{\uparrow}2 - 3)\uparrow (t + 1)$.

32. Verify that the tree structure given below is equivalent to the assignment statement

$$y \leftarrow (a \cdot b + c) \cdot (d + e)$$

if we start at the bottom of the tree and replace each operator by the result of its operation on the two operands immediately below.

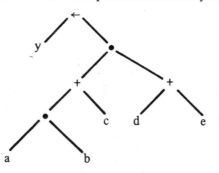

33. Produce the tree structures equivalent to the three assignment statements in Exercise 30.

7. Summary

A number of data structures have been considered in this chapter and in Chapter 10. An attempt has been made to relate the material to real applications areas. It must be emphasized, however, that in every situation simplifying assumptions were involved, either explicitly or implicitly, which made the problem under consideration relatively easy to treat. Such assumptions could not be used if we were working for a real company, government agency or other employer. Once these assumptions are removed there may be no best way to handle a particular problem. Each approach will have its good and its bad points and compromise will be the final result.

Clearly the duration of demand for the data and the amount of data involved will determine how much time is spent in analysis of the data structure to be used. In large applications it is not uncommon for hundreds of man years of effort to go into the design and implementation of a new data system. One of the major problems which must be solved is how a large system will interact with other information systems over which there is little or no control. A system which does not consider this problem has very little likelihood of functioning successfully. Hopefully, the costs of such analysis will be recovered in more efficient operation of the entire system. Unfortunately, in many cases, not enough effort is spent on this analysis and as a result the information system which is produced operates below the levels promised or does not function at all.

Since the exercises given at the end of the previous sections of this chapter were designed to require only a few minutes analysis it seems appropriate to give several problems in the final set of exercises whose magnitude will suggest the true scope of currently functional or proposed information retrieval systems.

Exercises

34. Explain how linked linear lists could be used to make the radix sorting method of Chapter 9 a more attractive internal sorting method by reducing the storage requirements of the method and also the data movements involved.

35. Write a program to produce the product of two polynomials if they are represented as in Exercise 20.

36. Every evening a man takes his dog for a walk. To avoid the monotony of traveling over the same route each night he flips a coin at each corner he comes to and goes left if it is heads and right if it is tails. Simulate the path that the man travels using a binary tree structure and

record where he is when he comes to the fourth corner. Run the simulation for 100 walks. If the man's house is on a corner and he always walks one block before flipping the coin the first time, what percentage of the time will he back home at the end of his walk? What will be his average distance from home if he takes the shortest route home without cutting through any yards?

37. Consider the problem in Exercise 36 again, but assume that the man carries a spinner on which the directions North, East, South, and West are marked. At each corner he uses this spinner to decide in which direction to travel next. Assume that each direction has equal probability of occurring.

38. Show the tree structure resulting from doing a binary search on the following set of data.

$$\{\, 3, 7, 8, 12, 13, 14, 15, 21, 42, 80 \,\}$$

If the numbers given above represent the item numbers in a company's inventory and the % of requests for each item is as given below

item no.	3	7	8	12	13	14	15	21	42	80
% of requests	5	20	5	15	5	5	10	25	5	5

what is the average number of comparisons per request?

39. Give a better tree structure for searching the data in Exercise 38. Why is it better?

40. Design an information system for handling all student records at a university with 35,000 students.

41. Design an information system to maintain records on 90,000 pieces of rolling stock making 100,000 movements per day over 17,000 miles of track passing through 76 major switching yards.

42. Design an information system for maintaining records on all New York stock exchange transactions.

43. Design a simulation model of the St. Lawrence Seaway from Quebec City to the Lakehead and Chicago.

44. Design a national credit rating information system.

45. Design a national information system for assisting police in their identification and control of criminals.

Further Reading

Annual Review of Information Science and Technology, Encyclopedia Britannica,

Chicago, Illinois (Vols. 1–4).

Bisco, R. L., *Data Bases, Computers, and the Social Sciences,* Wiley–Interscience, New York, 1970.

Dodd, G. G., "Elements of Data Management Systems," *Computing Surveys,* Vol. 1, No. 2 (June), 1969.

Forsythe, A. I. and T. A. Keenan, E. I. Organick, and W. Stenberg, *Computer Science: A First Course,* John Wiley, New York, 1969.

Gruenberger, F., (ed.), *Critical Factors in Data Management,* Prentice-Hall, Englewood Cliffs, New Jersey, 1969.

Hull, T. E. and D. D. F. Day, *Computers and Problem Solving,* Addison-Wesley (Canada) Ltd., Don Mills, Ontario, 1970.

Iverson, K. E., *A Programming Language,* John Wiley, New York, 1962.

Korfhage, R. R., *Logic and Algorithms,* John Wiley, New York, 1966.

Knuth, D. E., *The Art of Computer Programming,* Vol. 1, Fundamental Algorithms, Addison-Wesley, Reading, Massachusetts, 1968.

Rosove, P. E., *Developing Computer-Based Information Systems,* John Wiley, New York, 1967.

Index